E. C. Barrett

# Viewing Weather from Space

Can any understand the spreadings
of the clouds? (*Job 36: 29*)

**FREDERICK A. PRAEGER,** *Publishers*
New York · Washington

BOOKS THAT MATTER
Published in the United States of America in 1967
by Frederick A. Praeger, Inc., Publishers
111 Fourth Avenue, New York, N.Y. 10003

Library of Congress Catalog Card Number: 67–23367

*Printed in Great Britain*

Praeger Monographs in Geography

Viewing Weather from Space

Praeger Monographs in Geography

VIEWING WEATHER FROM SPACE    E. C. Barrett

*To my Father and Mother*
*for Everything*

# Foreword

The geography paperbacks series is concerned with the work and interests of geographers. Geography has always been a broad and diverse subject—therein lies its fascination and its stimulus for many of us. Part of its discipline lies in the mastery of certain cognate subjects, the understanding of which is essential to the full appreciation of the topic under discussion. Thus in the first of the series, *Migrants and Malaria*, Dr. R. M. Prothero went far into the fields of medical geography and of demography in Africa: doctors, sociologists, administrators and others besides geographers are interested in the work that he did and in the results of his investigations. Similarly Dr. E. S. Simpson's *Coal and the Power Industries in Postwar Britain*, the second book in the series, called for the careful handling and interpretation of statistics as well as for an assessment of the work of economists and engineers and a recognition of the significance of governmental changes of policy.

*Viewing Weather from Space* goes even further beyond the popular, and usually erroneous, concept of what geographers study and illustrates literally the tremendous range of a geographer's interest. The author graduated in geography in the University of Sheffield and then undertook research in climatology and biogeography. His thinking in these important branches of the subject aroused an interest in satellite meteorology, beginning, as he explains in his preface, by a realization of its usefulness as a teaching aid though by no means ending there. Two visits to the U.S.A. have introduced him to the wealth of instruments and research in American government and other establishments, and in this volume he seeks to share some of his discoveries with a public that is, in general, as ignorant of the subject as was the editor before he read the author's manuscript. The time has come for us to consider the surface of our planet from a new viewpoint, in Space. A new stimulus, and a new challenge, result from this ability to view the earth and its atmosphere in an entirely new perspective. In this geographers are concerned as well as meteorologists, physicists and mathematicians. If the first years of satellite meteorology lead towards a better comprehension of weather and of climate, and hasten the possibility of the control of weather on a global scale by man, then we are indeed living in exciting and epoch-making days.

ROBERT W. STEEL

Liverpool, January 1967

# Contents

# List of Plates

# Acknowledgements

We are indebted to the following for permission to reproduce copyright material:

G. Bell & Sons Ltd for lines from *The Clouds of Aristophanes* translated by B.B. Rogers, and Pan American World Airways for the 'Report from pilot's log'.

We are grateful to the following for permission to reproduce photographs:

National Aeronautics and Space Administration, Washington: Plates 1b, 2a; National Space Science Data Center, Maryland: Plates 3a, 3b, 7b, 8a, 8b; U.S. Department of Commerce, Environmental Science Services Administration: Frontispiece and plates 2b, 4a, 4b, 5a, 5b, 6, 7a, 7c–7f. Plate 1a is an official U.S. Navy photograph.

Diagrams have been based on copyright material as follows:

Fig 19 from J. C. Sadler *AFCRL—62—829*, August 1962; Fig. 7 from R. Stanipfl and H. Press, *Astronautics & Aeronautics*, July 1962; Fig. 14 from Bandeen et al., *NASA, TN D—2534*, June 1963; Fig. 10 from Bandeen et al., *Journal of Geophysical Research*, Vol. 66, p. 3171; Fig. 2 from AVCS Daily Coverage Map, 18 September 1964, Orbits 302–317, National Space Science Data Center; Fig 3 from *Weatherwise*, Vol 15, no. 3, 1962 by permission of the American Meteorological Society.

# PART ONE

# The Growth of a
# New Space-age Science

# 1  An Historical Perspective

The study of the weather must be as ancient as man's curiosity about his environment. From those far-off beginnings it has finally come of age in a twentieth-century scientific setting whose hallmarks are quantification, nuclear physics, and perhaps above all, the venture into Space.

During many centuries the vagaries of the weather must have continually surprised primitive food-gathering peoples whose intelligent awareness of the climatic environment was practically nil. If it is correct to assume that these earliest human societies were to be found in tropical regions, favoured by perpetual summer conditions, then they probably accepted the weather as a fairly stable environmental element, each day being like the one before. Later, as man became more intelligent—or more experienced—he began to modify his environment consciously by nursing the more useful plants, and developing close acquaintances with certain useful, docile animals. As he moved away from the constant warmth and ample rainfall of the humid tropics, so his need to understand the weather became more urgent.

Man is a religious being at heart, and it is not surprising that his first foray in search of a cause-and-effect understanding of the weather led him into the presence of the divine. In some early agricultural communities, such as that of the lower Nile valley, the most important environmental variable was not the weather, which varied little, but the great river itself, whose seasonal fluctuations, locally unrelated to climate, determined the yearly cycle of agricultural events. The Nile became an object of worship, and early irrigation engineers its priests. In other regions, however, local geographical variations were more obviously related to the weather, which itself was seen as the handiwork of the gods. It is hardly surprising that many of man's earliest attempts to understand, and modify, the weather reflected his belief in supernatural power—and the importance of keeping 'him' or 'them' in a pleasant frame of mind, even through the ultimate of human sacrifice.

In some ways it may seem that we have progressed little from that stage. There are still occasions when even the professional weathermen are surprised by the weather, despite the elaborate facilities that are now available for observation, data processing, and scientific analysis of the results. Human lives may no longer be offered for the propitiation or conciliation of the unseen powers of the air, but this is not to say that the weather cannot cause civilised societies to behave in an apparently primitive fashion. In a later chapter reference is made to an attempt to imprison a weather forecaster for a forecast that was fatally incorrect. One can sense a reflection of ancient practices here, even though, in the modern world the need is to conciliate the emotions of human society rather than those of a god! The 'shadow of the Almighty' is still cast over legal proceedings, where an 'act of God' remains a legitimate plea for the exoneration of damages to persons or property, should the circumstances be so exceptional that they could not have been foreseen. And in South Africa early in 1966 prolonged drought became the subject of a national day of prayer for rain. The sequel was rain in such abundance that some parts of the country were flooded a day later. In Old Testament times this would, no doubt, have been recorded as a miracle!

In many other ways, however, great advances in understanding the weather have lessened its ability to surprise and bewilder. Weather study has progressed far along scientific lines. It involves observation, classification, the formulation of hypotheses, the development of weather models, and, by virtue of the first tentative steps to modify the weather over a wide area, weather control. The fundamental *sine qua non* is that of *observation*. Indeed, it can be claimed that the growth periods in man's comprehension of the weather have been linked almost invariably with some major advance in observation, whether this involved personal awareness and verbal description of weather events, or advances in mathematical theory and instrument-

# Preface

The primary purpose of this book is to draw the attention of all who have an interest in the weather, amateur and professional alike, to the general usefulness of specialised weather satellites. The account does not attempt to mention every line of investigation that has already been traced through the enormous volume of new data that has begun to flood back from Space. Nor does it pretend to be a textbook of meteorology. It discusses the new weather observational systems in considerable detail so that their capabilities can be critically assessed; it illustrates the usefulness of the new data in pure and applied meteorology, in research and weather forecasting; it places the satellites in their historical perspective, by reviewing weather study through bygone centuries, and by taking a look at the most likely developments in the foreseeable future; and, since it is written by a geographer, there are references to the scope for geographical research in satellite meteorology and climatology, as well as a discussion of some of the types of surface features on the world of man that can be studied with benefit from Space.

The atmosphere is a vitally important part of man's natural environment. Of the 'eternal triangle' of soils, vegetation and climate, climate is the most prone to relatively rapid change, and can be claimed to be the most basic variable of the three. New brands of geography and new breeds of geographers seem to be appearing with increasing frequency as our knowledge of the world proliferates, but there can be few, if any, fields of study within the discipline that are not affected in some way by the weather.

It is important, therefore, that developments in weather observation, forecasting, and research should be widely recognised in geographical circles. This account, describing some of the most exciting developments in meteorology for a long while, has been written as far as possible in descriptive terms that should be understandable to most, although the use of less familiar terms has often been unavoidable. Whereas many of the phenomena to which they refer are explained in the text, some prior knowledge of the atmosphere and its workings has had to be assumed, since otherwise there would have been no room left to consider weather satellite systems, and consequent contributions to meteorological thought.

Initially, my own interest in satellite meteorology arose from the realisation that here was an innovation of potentially supreme usefulness in teaching. Cloud photographs portraying large-scale weather complexes bring into the lecture room a new sense of the reality of textbook mysteries such as hurricanes and the intertropical convergence zone. But one cannot handle satellite material long without many research topics springing to mind, and some of these I am following up myself. In the U.S.A. many research workers are analysing satellite data; there is great scope in this field, and an urgent need for other studies to be carried out, throughout the world. Perhaps this book will help to stimulate more scientists—meteorologists, physicists, mathematicians, and geographers—to think along these lines.

I should like to thank the staff of the National Weather Satellite Laboratory in the U.S. Weather Bureau, Suitland, Maryland for many stimulating discussions during my visit there. My particular thanks go to Dr. Carl O. Erickson for his friendship and help in resolving a number of points of detail in the text. Mr. J.L.H. Sibbons of the Geography Department in the University of Sheffield, a former teacher and colleague of mine, read and commented upon the manuscript, for which generous help I am very grateful. To Professor R.W. Steel go my thanks for his initial interest in the theme of the book, and for his encouragement at every stage in its production. Finally, I should like to acknowledge the contribution made towards my visit to the U.S. Weather Bureau from the Travelling Fund of the University of Bristol.

The contents of the book have been drawn from many sources, some published, others not, from personal studies, and from discussions with experts in this country and the U.S.A. Each chapter ends with a list of the more important, and most readily accessible, works that have been consulted, and the reader may follow the main themes of the text in more detail through those references.

Perhaps the biggest problem has been the compilation of an account that will not date too rapidly, a difficult problem to resolve in a field of rapid progress and already copious publication. It has been resolved by presenting the information as a survey of the first six years of satellite meteorology, from April 1960 when TIROS I was launched, to February 1966 when the first fully operational weather satellites were put into orbit, thus concluding the 'experimental period' and bringing into being a system capable of viewing the whole world's weather at least once every day. Some of the techniques and research implications outlined here may be outdated quickly, but most should hold good for several years to come.

E.C. BARRETT
Dartmouth, Devon

ation. It is possible, therefore, to outline a history of the study of the earth's atmosphere under six headings:

## The developing awareness of weather as a composite phenomenon

From the variability of the Mediterranean weather there grew up in the early years of the ancient Greek civilisation a whole multitude of gods who both controlled, and reflected in their appearances, the various aspects of the weather. Government of the physical world was no longer in the hands of a single river god, but in a triumvirate of divinities—Poseidon, or Neptune, ruled the sea and its shores; Hades or Pluto was the guardian of the hollows, caves, mines and minerals of the underworld; and Zeus, or Jupiter, ruled the skies. Under the command of Jupiter, a whole host of mythical personifications of the weather soon arose. The goddess Medusa, or Gorgon, for example, was a very apt personification of a winter cyclone in the Mediterranean region. The coil of a snake, describing Medusa's hair, is an excellent portrayal of the circulation into a temperate depression, or the spiral pattern of clouds curling into the centre of an occluding cyclone as seen from satellite altitudes. The very word 'cyclone' is embodied in the Greek expression for a coiled snake. Could the Greeks really have understood the structure of a cyclone sufficiently well for this particular likeness to have been deliberate? Or was it an amazing piece of intuitive insight into weather organisation? Or a coincidentally appropriate poetic sixth sense?

The fact that various weather types were being distinguished from each other represented a big advance, but, as Critchfield succinctly says 'little progress could be made in recognising or understanding sequences of weather whilst the Gods held sway, for they were predictable only in terms of their reactions to the pleasure or displeasure humans caused them,—and even these relationships could only be worked out in retrospect!'

## The revolution of systematic observation

In the fifth century B.C. the Greeks began to make regular meteorological observations, and the official view of the weather was displayed by means of the 'parapegma', a kind of peg-almanac that was affixed to public columns for all to see. The most important observations concerned the direction and force of the wind, natural choices for a peninsular society with a keen interest in navigation. This period saw the earliest development of the wind vane, and a variety of devices for collecting and measuring rainfall.

3

It was not long before the philosophically minded Greeks were able to attempt some of the first prognostic statements concerning the weather, in the first conscious effort to move from observation to objective weather forecasting. The contemporaneous loosening of the old shackles of multi-theistic weather explanation permitted deeper thought along scientific lines, and meteorology and climatology were born. The names themselves reflect their Greek beginnings, the former representing a discourse on 'things above', the latter a discussion of the atmospheric effects of the supposed 'klima' or slope of the earth, thought by the Greeks to be the cause of many differences in climate from one place to another.

The new attitude towards the weather soon bore fruit in the scientific writings of ancient Greece. Hippocrates, for example, has left a medical climatology written about 400 B.C. entitled *Airs, Waters and Places,* and Aristotle attempted a systematic exposition of the new field of study in his remarkable *Meteorologica* written some fifty years later. Some indication of the magnitude of the revolution in weather study that resulted from the new approach of the ancient Greeks can be gleaned from the following extract from the comedy of *The Clouds* by Aristophanes. The dialogue is between Strepsiades, a countryman clinging to the 'orthodox' religious beliefs, and Socrates, representing the new group of rationalist philosophers. The subjects under discussion were the causes of rain and thunder.

STREPSIADES: No Zeus up aloft in the sky!
Then you first must explain who it is sends the rain,
Or I really must think you are wrong.

SOCRATES: Well, then, be it known, these (the clouds) send it alone
I can prove it by arguments strong.
Was there ever a shower seen to fall in an hour
When the sky was all cloudless and blue?
Yet on a fine day, when the Clouds are away,
He might send one, according to you.

STREPSIADES: But is it not He who compels this to be?
Does not Zeus this Necessity send?

SOCRATES: No Zeus have we there, but a Vortex of air.

STREPSIADES: What! Vortex? that's something I own
I knew not before, that Zeus was no more,
But Vortex was placed on his throne!
But I have not yet heard

To what cause you referred
The Thunder's majestical roar.

SOCRATES: Yes, 'tis they, when on high,
Full of water they fly,
And then, as I told you before,
By compression impelled, as they clash,
Are compelled, a terrible clatter to make.

There are many peoples throughout the world who still consider that thunder is the angry voice of the gods. Socrates' explanation of cause and effect may leave much to be desired from a modern scientific point of view, but compared with common superstitious beliefs both then and now, it is a measure of the truly remarkable advance that had been made already in meteorology as a result of critical weather observation and objective philosophy.

## The experience of centuries—
## the development of weather lore

With the decline in the civilisation of ancient Greece, there was a decline in philosophical thought also, and the next few centuries were comparatively barren from a scientific point of view. The study of the weather, however, continued in the hands of Romans and Christian thinkers, but most significantly in the corporate thoughts of whole nations of people. At least in the temperate latitudes men were fully aware of the weather, and although few instrumental or conscious systematic observations were made, there developed an observational system that included the various classes of society, each of which noted those relationships between wind and weather that affected them directly in their daily work. This was the period above all others during which weather lore crystallised out, this expressing pithily the observations of the multitudes and their accumulated experience in prognostics. In the Greek world authoritative pronouncements concerning the weather had been the concern of the few; from then until the Renaissance every man and each society had to be expert. Weather study was not revolutionised as abruptly as before, but the general level of weather awareness and understanding rose quietly and unobtrusively and enabled men in most walks of life to recognise intuitively, or by the experience that was handed on from one generation to the next, the weather developments that were likely a day or two ahead.

Since then the aptness of many of the weather proverbs that abound in this country and throughout Europe has been demon-

5

strated time and again. Some obviously reflect the suggestions of divine control that were prevalent earlier, but many must have developed free from restrictions of that kind. The least successful statements of weather lore are those that attempt to predict the more distant future, yet these may be no less successful than some modern methods of long-range weather forecasting! Students of climatic change have yet to disprove some of the more adventurous sayings, such as that relating the height of rooks' nests to the calms or storms of the coming summer, and other long-range proverbial pronouncements are now thought to contain previously unsuspected elements of truth. In France there is a medieval proverb stating wryly that 'weather, wind, women and fortune change like the moon'. Some authorities now claim that a non-random relationship connects rainfall with the phases of the moon, and this claim is based upon the stringent statistical investigation of reliable data. Perhaps the French proverb is more accurate, weatherwise at least, than one might think at first.

Whereas today great reliance in long-range forecasting is placed upon the memory store of an electronic brain, in the past the memory store was the memory of the nation. It is to be regretted that the general level of weather awareness in Britain today is almost certainly lower than it formerly was; modern technology serves to insulate man increasingly from his climatic environment, both in terms of how he lives, and what he does for a living.

The Renaissance, with which this period of weather lore was to end, compared with the golden age of Greece in the speed of its advances in scientific and philosophical thought. By comparison, the intervening centuries are often dismissed as a period of stagnation, but this is less than justice. In fact it can be claimed that the brilliant insight into so many things that characterised the talented individuals of the Renaissance required a prelude during which the insight of the whole community was raised. If this was so, then these preceding centuries were not ones of stagnation or regression, but of slow revolution, during which many of the meteorological notions of earlier thinkers, such as the ancient Greeks, were consolidated into more popular forms. Certainly some mistaken ideas did become fossilised in weather lore, and still others first appeared therein, but over the period as a whole, significant progress was made.

## The first technological revolution in weather study

The Renaissance was a remarkable phenomenon by any standard. Every aspect of art and science, whether fine or liberal, pure or applied, was affected. To the student of the atmosphere the Renaissance was important primarily on account of the new instruments that were made available to him, enabling him to measure a greater variety of weather elements with precision. Two instruments are worthy of special mention, namely the thermometer designed by Galileo in 1593, and the mercurial barometer, the principle of which was discovered by his equally famous pupil Torricelli. Once it became possible to measure changes in weather elements in a standardised fashion, the weather in different localities could be compared without feeling that maybe the views of the observers concerning, for example, warmth and coldness differed too, and that any attempted comparison was spurious as a result.

Despite the great progress that was made thus, many years elapsed before measurements from widely scattered stations could be co-ordinated quickly enough for scientific forecasting to commence. Indeed, the technological developments of the Renaissance were slow to be capitalised upon, and even by 1800 there were probably no more than a dozen reliable stations in Europe making routine temperature and pressure observations, and in the United States the number was only half as great. Technical developments in other fields were to play their own vital part.

## The revolution in communications

1832 is a highly significant date, for that year saw the invention of telegraphy. At last a system was available whereby weather data could be gathered from a large number of widely disseminated stations within minutes of the observations being made. This new development, assisted later by radio, led directly to a rapid multiplication of weather stations linked to central forecasting offices, making possible the study of entire weather systems in much greater detail than ever before. This led to the development of more sophisticated model concepts, and man's understanding of the weather steadily deepened. In the middle of the nineteenth century a German, Henrich Wilhelm Dove, better known for his pioneer attempt at climatic classification, first developed the concept of the involvement of polar and tropical air masses in the formation of extratropical depressions. This, and other similarly significant conceptual developments were to pave the way for the more detailed work of the twentieth century. Sir Francis Galton, sometimes styled 'the Father of British Meteorology', drew attention during the American Civil War to the existence of anticyclones, whose high pressure and relatively calm conditions had tended to be overlooked, with man's

7

attention held firmly by the more dramatic mobile low pressure storms. And, to cite only one more example of the many concepts formulated scientifically during the nineteenth century, the Dutch admiral Buys-Ballot stated in 1857 his famous rule relating the local distribution of centres of high and low pressure to the direction of wind flow. The various revolutions in the study of the weather were at last beginning to yield much fruit, and spasmodic research was giving way to a carefully planned progressive assault upon the many mysteries of atmospheric behaviour.

The First World War gave an added incentive to synoptic weather analysis, and kites and balloons were applied to the investigation of the vertical structure of the atmosphere. The development of the weather map finally established forecasting as a science in its own right, with its own problems and procedures. Three-dimensional studies were further aided by aircraft, which enable man to change his viewpoint and fly through and above the cloud systems associated with various pressure and air mass patterns. A more detailed knowledge of the upper atmosphere helped to place surface weather into a more complete perspective, and the work of Carl-Gustav Rossby and others brought to light important relationships between pressure and temperature patterns at various altitudes. These three-dimensional studies received further impetus during the Second World War, and the potential of radar for tracking belts of rain was quickly realised, another important step forward in the observation of weather over a wide area. Radar capable of investigating regions hundreds of miles in diameter has since been developed, in order to portray rainfall patterns in a detail that could never be achieved with a mere array of 'conventional' weather stations.

## The space-age revolution

Since the end of the Second World War has unfolded the period during which both instruments and men have been put semi-permanently into Space, a revolution whose true scientific potential can still only be surmised. When peace was finally secured in 1945, German techniques in rocketry were adopted for application to a variety of non-military scientific projects. In the last two decades, cameras have been pointed earthwards with increasing frequency from altitudes of fifty miles and more, very much higher than aircraft can venture. Some of the new photographs portrayed cloud-free conditions, and were interesting primarily from a geological point of view. Many, however, showed well-organised cloud extending over hundreds or maybe even thousands of miles, some confirming

8

hypotheses developed from ground recordings of the weather, whereas others suggested relationships of a kind and on a scale unimagined theretofore. A whole variety of rockets whose names will be familiar in other contexts have been used in these first high-altitude investigations of the weather—Viking, Nike-Cajun, and Aerobee figuring prominently amongst them.

One of the biggest problems concerning photography from Space is the recovery of the photographic information. The rockets themselves being recoverable, employed cassettes of good quality aero-film and yielded photographs high in quality and good in resolution. (See Plate 1a.) Similarly, the very temporary earth-satellites of the Gemini series have contributed good quality photographs (see Plate 1b)—in colour too—taken by the American astronauts, and recovered on their return to earth. In the case of higher-altitude, more permanent satellites, such as those described in this book, different photographic techniques become necessary, involving television and radio systems of transmission and recovery. Additional equipment, measuring infra-red radiation from the earth and its atmosphere is included in some permanent weather spacecraft. This equipment is designed to investigate large-scale patterns of temperature.

It is the view of the author that satellites compare with the first barometers and thermometers of the Renaissance period in terms of their implications for weather observation. The latest satellites are providing a complete view of the world's weather at least once every day, surveying land and sea, industrial nation and polar ice-cap alike, and new forecasting procedures are being developed as a result. The satellite ability to demonstrate the general structure of every type of weather system, from the smallest to the largest, following their growth, decay, and paths of motion, has already been capitalised in much meteorological and climatological research.

One of the characteristic features of the earlier revolutionary developments in weather observation was that their true significance was usually slow to be recognised. New ideas and new instruments were slow to be adopted generally. It would be extremely unfortunate if the use of satellites was similarly slow to meet with widespread approval. Many countries have already expressed an interest in weather satellite systems, but there is the danger that this may represent no more than a honeymoon period whilst the novelty and news values are high. Much hard thinking will be required before something approaching the true potential is realised in everyday meteorology, but, as this book seeks to show, the first six years, comprising the 'experimental phase' of satellite meteorology, have been years full of interest and encouragement. As the resolution of the satellite data is improved, so even more emphasis should be placed on satellite studies.

## The final revolution

One major revolution remains to be achieved, and with it the dream and goal of many down through the centuries, namely the control and modification of the weather on a global scale. The modifications that can be made in local micro-climates represent no more than the beginning. For the scale of control to be extended, however, the fullest possible use must be made of every observational system available to man so that the workings of the weather can be more fully understood. Exactly when the final revolution will be possible one cannot say. Much that is unknown must be made clear before Charles Kingsley's famous rhyme can be rewritten thus:

Who is it moulds the course of the weather?
The Weatherman.
Who makes some black and others tan?
The Weatherman.
Who made the Zulus leave their trees
And Congo natives shed their leaves
While none need go in furs and freeze?
The Weatherman.
'Tis the English Weatherman
Breeds modern Englishmen.

Then, and only then, will man be the true master of his climatic environment.

BIBLIOGRAPHY
One of the most detailed and comprehensive texts concerned with the history of meteorology is by Napier Shaw, *Meteorology in History*, Vol. I, 1924, in the *Manual of Meteorology* published by the Cambridge University Press. See also H.J. Critchfield, *General Climatology*, Prentice-Hall, 1960, chapter 1, 3. The development of modern observation systems is described by J.G. Vaeth, *Weather Eyes in the Sky*, Ronald Press, New York, 1965. A useful summary of different kinds of space photography is by J.B. Bird and A. Morrison, 'Space photography and its geographical applications', *Geographical Review*, 54, 1964, 463. See also E.C. Barrett, 'Viewing weather from space',

*Geographical Magazine*, **38**, 1965, 195. For an exhaustive bibliography of articles relating to meteorology from Space until 1963, see the 'Supplementary bibliography on the use of satellites in Meteorology', *Meteorological and Geoastrophysical Abstracts*, **14**, 1963, 870.

# 2 Weather Satellite Systems

Since the Russians shocked the world by launching the first artificial satellite in 1957, many spacecraft have made observations of interest to the meteorologist, but mostly in invisible regions of the electro-magnetic spectrum. Although as a result many contributions have been made to man's knowledge of the upper atmosphere in particular, by far the greatest contributions to weather study have been made by the two families of American satellites designed specifically for weather observation. It is upon these two systems, TIROS and NIMBUS, that the attention of this book is primarily focused. The type and quantity of the information obtained from them obviously depends upon their design features, and although it is not necessary to examine the technical aspects of satellite engineering too minutely, a brief account of satellite configuration, the characteristics of various orbital paths, and the meteorological recording equipment will serve as an explanatory introduction to the analysis and use of the data.

## The TIROS satellites and their orbits

The first of the TIROS family was blasted off from the then Cape Canaveral in Florida early in the morning of April 1st 1960, atop a three-stage Thor-Able rocket complex. The launcher functioned well, and TIROS I was placed into its planned near circular orbit some 450 statute miles above the surface of the earth. At that altitude each journey around the world was to take about 100 minutes, a programme which was to be followed closely by eight of the subsequent nine TIROS satellites launched between 1960 and the end of 1965. In fact the first eight TIROS occupied orbits that varied in only one important respect, namely the angles at which they were inclined to the equator. Table 1 (p. 129) shows that the first four orbited at 48° to the equator, and these were intended to yield information of tropical weather patterns in particular. TIROS V to VIII orbited at the slightly higher angle of 58°. Although polar and high latitudinal regions therefore went unobserved, the preferential treatment that the tropics enjoyed for four years helped to focus the attention of research upon areas whose meteorological conditions are relatively little known and inadequately understood. One significant practical reason for the selection of a rather low oblique angled orbit with which to begin was the urgent need to spot, track, and forecast the paths of highly destructive tropical storms approaching the

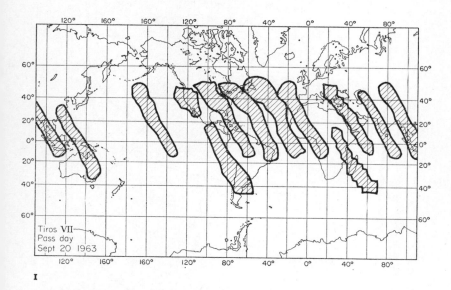

I

Caribbean region and the south-eastern corner of the U.S.A. in late summer and autumn in particular. Fig. 1, taken from an official catalogue, shows the areas covered observationally during one twenty-four hour period by a TIROS satellite in a 58°-orbit. TIROS IX and X, the forerunners of the present operational satellite system, were placed into quasi-polar orbits, at angles of 80° to the equator. These, along with NIMBUS I, whose orbit was also near-polar, were the first to make possible a nearly complete global view of the earth's surface each day, as illustrated by Fig. 2.

Another important way in which the orbits differed depended upon the configuration of the satellites themselves. Fig. 3 is a schematic plan of a 'standard' TIROS, whose spin axis is orientated towards a fixed point in Space. The first eight were of this type. The general shape and size has been likened to a large hat-box,

13

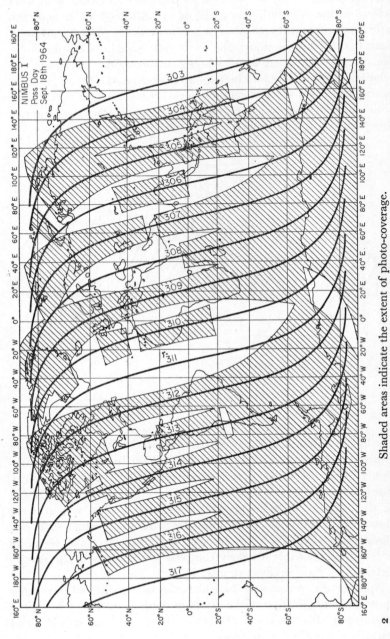

Shaded areas indicate the extent of photo-coverage.

measuring 42 inches in diameter and 22½ inches in depth. The side walls are covered with more than 9,000 solar cells, whose normal electrical output is 20 watts. This is the energy supply by which the radio apparatus, and meteorological equipment is powered. This equipment consists of television cameras and infra-red radiation sensors, accompanied by tape-recording circuits for storing data, hence the name TIROS, which is an acronym of Television and

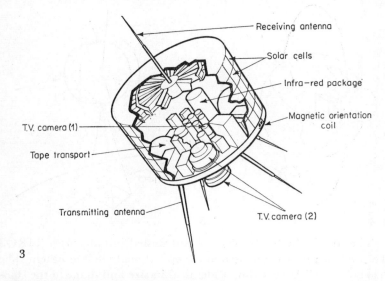

Receiving antenna

Solar cells

Infra–red package

Magnetic orientation coil

T.V. camera (1)

Tape transport

Transmitting antenna

T.V. camera (2)

3

Infra-Red Observation Satellite. Two television cameras are employed in each, and these point outwards through the baseplate, and are themselves orientated towards Space as a result. Consequently few photographs taken by them are vertical views of the earth (see Plate 2a), whereas many are quite low obliques. For approximately one-half of each orbit the cameras actually point away into Space as shown diagrammatically in Fig. 4. Provided that the desired attitude of the satellite relative to the earth is achieved during launching, Space orientation does not place too great a restriction upon weather photography since one-half of the world is in darkness at any time, and the cameras could not function usefully then even if they were to be pointed at the earth. The rotation of the earth enables it to present a fresh zone to be photographed on each successive orbit, so that most areas between latitudes of about 60° north and south can be photographed daily by a standard satellite with an orbital period of about 100 minutes, and suitably chosen camera lens apertures. The problem of the increasing obliquity of the photographs away from the equatorial zone represents the most serious shortcoming, since photo-interpretation is greatly complicated thereby. This is a problem that will be discussed in more detail in Chapter 3. The interpretation of satellite photographs is facilitated by a constant camera angle relative to the earth, and two different weather satellite schemes have already demonstrated ways in which this characteristic can be achieved.

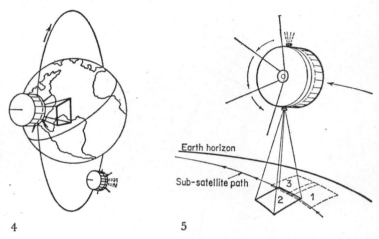

Earth horizon

Sub-satellite path

4                                      5

The first is the 'cartwheel' variant, tested initially with TIROS IX, and currently being used in the operational satellite system. The 'cartwheel' TIROS is almost identical in size and shape to the standard TIROS, but its own spin axis is perpendicular to its plane of orbit. In other words, it rolls around the world on its side in cartwheel fashion. Its television cameras do not parallel the spin axis as in the standard configuration, but are arranged so that they point outwards through the side walls. They can be programmed to operate from a chosen angle with the earth's surface, as shown in Fig. 5. They are in fact set at angles of 26° to the perpendicular, so that the photographs from the two cameras may be fitted together in pairs thus covering a wider area across the sub-satellite path than if the views were from the perpendicular itself. Since the angles relative to the earth are constant, problems of graticuling and interpreting the photographs are very much more simple than with the 'standard' system, and, of course, there is an absence of very low oblique images. It is true that the scale of each pair of photographs varies from the camera sub-points to the picture margins, but the variation is not large enough to worry the experienced interpreter. Plate 2b exemplifies this type of photography.

16

The 'cartwheel' satellites have all employed quasi-polar orbits at
angles of about 100° to the equator.

## NIMBUS weather satellites

The second type of satellite maintaining a constant camera angle
with the earth's surface is the more elaborate and more expensive
NIMBUS. Fig. 6 illustrates its greater complexity compared with
the TIROS type. The most striking modification involves the re-
deployment of solar cells, here arranged in two large paddles, which

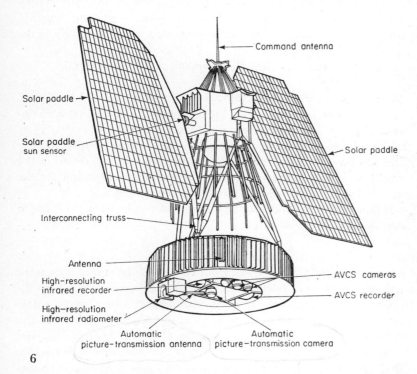

6

can be oriented constantly towards the sun by the sun sensors at
their bases. This is a much more efficient arrangement than in
TIROS, the 11,000 cells deployed in NIMBUS yielding a maximum
400 watts of electrical energy, representing a twentyfold increase in
power. Otherwise, the instrument-carrying portion is basically similar to a standard TIROS satellite excepting in the number of
cameras carried (four instead of two), and the more advanced type
of infra-red sensor.

The NIMBUS flight pattern was also advanced compared with

17

TIROS. First, NIMBUS was conceived as an 'earth orientated' satellite whose central axis was always pointing down vertically to the surface of the earth. Second, whereas TIROS was stabilised by spinning about its own axis, a new control system enabled NIMBUS to orbit in a stable manner without this kind of spin. The NIMBUS pattern of photography depended on the success of this new control system, since the three television cameras viewed the earth through the satellite base plate, and were arranged to take triplets of photographs at right angles to the direction of satellite movement. Although only one NIMBUS was placed in orbit during the experimental period, that satellite pioneered several new instruments, and the same configuration will be used as a test bed for others in the future.

Table 1 (p. 129) summarises some of these satellite details.

## Weather satellite meteorological equipment

Although the satellites are all highly sophisticated pieces of engineering, and include several separate systems and subsystems, only two of these need be described in detail in the present context, namely the television, and the infra-red. Readers who are interested in the engineering details are referred to the technical notes and articles listed in the bibliography at the end of the chapter.

Three different photographic systems are employed in the TIROS and NIMBUS satellites:

THE VIDICON CAMERA SYSTEM

Most of the TIROS spacecraft from 1960 until the end of 1965 were equipped with two independent camera chains, either of which included a television camera, a magnetic tape-recorder, and a transmitter. The cameras could operate separately or simultaneously. A similar system is currently employed by one of the two operational TIROS-type spacecraft. Table 2 (p. 129) lists the various lens angles that have been employed, and the areas covered by single frames from each. The resolution of a photograph depends largely upon the camera lens angle, so that the narrow-angled cameras (lens aperture 12·5°) cover smaller areas in greater detail than the wide-angled cameras (lens aperture 104°). The data in Table 1 are based on the assumption that the photography is vertical; if the angle is oblique, the area viewed is larger, and the resolution decreases towards the horizon.

The satellites receive their instructions from ground units known as the Command and Data Acquisition (C.D.A.) stations, and these

18

programme the photography and interrogate the satellites for the results. The equipment at a tracking station is basically very simple, consisting of a radio transmitter, and a receiver linked with a television screen. Within the satellite, the television cameras are so designed that each photographic image may be retained for several seconds after exposure, during which time they are read off line by line, and are transmitted directly to the ground if a C.D.A. station is within radio range. Here each picture is rebuilt on the television screen, and recorded permanently by means of a 35 mm camera which photographs the screen. The intervals at which successive pictures were taken by the experimental TIROS were generally either 10 or 30 seconds, the camera tube and the television receiver being automatically cleaned in between.

When a satellite passes out of the radio range of a C.D.A. station, it can continue to take photographs at programmed intervals and store the information on magnetic tape ready for playback when the next C.D.A. station comes into contact with it. The TIROS vidicon system is designed to store up to thirty-two pictures in sequence in this way, permitting the recovery of information concerning areas remote from North America; the three most extensively used C.D.A. stations being at Fairbanks in Alaska, Point Mugu in California, and Wallops Island in Virginia.

Photographs can, therefore, be obtained either by a 'direct camera' command, causing the images to bypass the recording circuit, or a 'tape' command which entails a time-lag between the photography itself and the playback of the pictorial data. Accompanying each photograph, in whichever way it is obtained, the satellite transmits information concerning the rotational position of the satellite and the angle of the sun at the instant the observation was made. This information is important in compiling an appropriate geographic locator grid prior to the interpretation of the photograph. It is relatively easy to locate the area depicted when some recognisable land mass is visible, but other factors must be taken into account when the area is ocean or overcast.

THE ADVANCED VIDICON CAMERA SYSTEM

This was pioneered by NIMBUS I, and is currently employed in other NIMBUS and operational TIROS-type satellites. Its main claim to be an 'advanced' system rests mainly on its use of an 800-line television receiver instead of the 500-line receivers used by the earlier TIROS. Apart from the aperture of the camera lens, a major factor affecting picture resolution is the number of lines on the television receiver at the C.D.A. station. Generally speaking, the greater the number of lines, the more detail that should be apparent, assuming a constant lens angle. The NIMBUS advanced camera system photographs were of startlingly good quality. Three of the cameras in NIMBUS I were of this kind, and were placed in the satellite in a fan-like array, taking photographs simultaneously of three slightly overlapping areas as shown in Fig. 7. When fitted together in mosaic form, each triplet spread across 107° of longitude

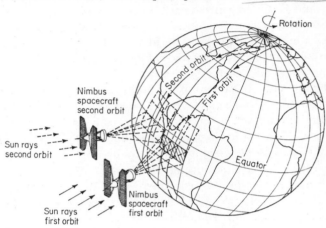

7

and 37° of latitude at the equator, the longitudinal spread obviously increasing polewards. The sets of photographs were taken at intervals of 90 seconds. Sufficient storage space on tape was allowed for the accommodation of a complete pole-to-pole sequence of photographs across the daylight hemisphere. Unfortunately the planned circular orbit at an altitude of 930 km was not achieved, but instead an elliptical orbit with a 932 km apogee, and a perigee of only 423 km —less than half that desired. As a result, many photographs were obtained from a rather low altitude, and the areas covered by them were, therefore, often separated by gaps in the picture coverage in equatorial regions, the overlap increasing towards the poles.

### THE AUTOMATIC PICTURE TAKING SYSTEM

This system, pioneered by the fourth camera in NIMBUS I, and the two cameras in TIROS VIII, is considerably different from the previous two. The biggest disadvantages of the C.D.A.—vidicon systems were the costs of the tracking stations, valued at about £$\frac{1}{3}$ million. This was prohibitively high for many of the countries wishing to partake eventually in an operational weather satellite system by obtaining their own pictures directly from the spacecraft. A new scheme was devised, therefore, which permitted the commissioning of the cameras by much simpler tracking stations, which employed radio facsimile methods of picture reproduction instead of costly television processes. Facsimile images are built up in dot, rather than in line, fashion, using ordinary mass-produced facsimile equipment similar to that used, for example, by various national news-

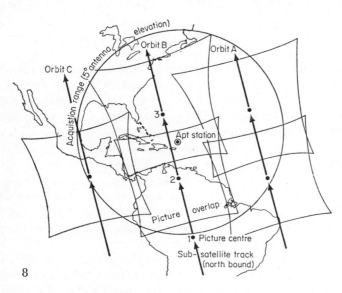

8

papers for the receipt of pictures by radio from other parts of the world. Scansion of the face of the camera tube in the satellite is slower, however, and 200 seconds are required for each picture to be read off dot by dot. This reduces the frequency with which photographs can be taken, but a total of three received by an A.P.T. station from a single satellite pass is quite sufficient to portray the weather over a large local area, as shown by Fig. 8. Although television pictures and the summary cloud charts compiled from them, can be transmitted or transported within a matter of hours to most parts of the world from the C.D.A. stations in the U.S.A., the A.P.T. system has the great advantage of being able to provide national meteorological centres with a pictorial representation of the weather in their own locality in only a tiny fraction of that time. The A.P.T. images, obtained in a semipermanent form on facsimile paper, do deteriorate with time, but they can be photographed for preservation purposes if they are of sufficient interest. Their primary usefulness is in *short-term* weather forecasting. Plate 3a is an A.P.T. photograph.

## Handling the photographs

Before the photographs can be used by the forecaster or research worker it is necessary that they should be gridded. Clearly the scientist wishes to know as accurately as possible such things as the positions of depression centres or hurricanes, and the alignment of cloud lines or bands. One of the earliest computer-assisted tasks in the handling of weather satellite data was the preparation of geographic grids, showing selected parallels and meridians, as transparent overlays.

A number of different facts need to be known before an accurate grid can be constructed. Of these, the attitude of the satellite and its own rotational position have already been mentioned. Others include the geographical bearings of the satellite sub-point, and the satellite's altitude when the picture was taken. Sometimes it is difficult to obtain all this information, and a large dictionary of coastlines has been built up, from which it is possible to make transformations to match the perspective of the photograph. This dictionary is often an invaluable aid in the task of grid construction, especially in the case of Space-orientated satellites. Transparent grids have been prepared for most of the photographs taken by the earlier satellites and are available for research purposes.

A simplified version of the gridding procedure is now carried out by smaller computers at the main TIROS television read-out stations, preparing grids for immediate use in connection with new forecasting techniques. The grids that are produced form the bases for the cloud charts that are compiled from each mosaiced sequence of photographs. Significant cloud features are traced off the photographs, in outline or symbol form, and are then replotted on a standard map base before the charts are transmitted to forecasting centres all over the world.

Experimental means have also been designed to rectify images that have been distorted in various ways. One of the distortions that can be corrected quite readily is a symmetrical distortion due to the shape of the camera lens and the satellite electronics system. The nature of the required calibration is determined by pre-launch calibration target photographs taken by the actual satellite cameras. Another procedure had to be developed to rectify the foreshortening that characterises Space-orientated photography, and the results were quite encouraging in all except the lowest oblique cases. Where the

22

camera angle was so low that the horizon was in view, the rectified images contained a good deal of interpolated 'filler' material probably bearing little relationship to reality. Extremes of this kind do not occur where earth-orientated satellites of the NIMBUS type are concerned, nor where TIROS satellites are placed into cartwheel orbits, so that this was only a temporary problem, and most photographs that are now being obtained from Space are not so oblique that rectification is necessary.

The camera system in NIMBUS posed different problems from those in the two types of TIROS. Perspective grids are required for the two lateral cameras, and a more regular grid for the central camera, which views the earth's surface from a vertical position. Since the attitude of all three cameras is theoretically constant, the grids can be prepared in advance, and superimposed upon the photographs as they are received at the tracking stations. The photographs can, therefore, be gridded in detail before the forecaster receives them, a technical development of no small importance.

It is hoped that the whole process, from the reception of the photographs from Space, to the production of a weather forecast based both on them, and conventional information, may one day be completely automatic. For this to be possible, a machine procedure for the analysis of the salient features of the cloud photographs would be required. This would involve scanning them both vertically and horizontally, to assess the variations in brightness, and the different patterns of cloudiness. It will be necessary for many photographs to be analysed manually in the first instance, so that the more repetitive cloud patterns and arrangements can be recognised. These must be related to pressure patterns, and then included amongst the features for which a computer can be programmed to search. This kind of study does not involve meteorological factors alone. The influences of topography must be taken into account also, for example, the influences of land and sea surfaces, lakes, mountain ranges, ocean currents, and areas of ice and snow. There is scope here for the geographer to assist the meteorologist in photo analysis.

The degree of accuracy that has been achieved in locating weather systems from satellite photographs can be illustrated with reference to the rather small, tightly coiled hurricanes that frequent the tropical oceans especially in late summer. These are highly destructive storms, so the means whereby they may be tracked have been considered carefully. Whilst the area covered by a single wide-angled TIROS photograph taken from an altitude of 500 miles is at least 750 miles square, the usual error in fixing the centre of a hurricane tends to be of the order of 50 nautical miles. This is a very reasonable figure when all the attendant difficulties are considered. There are several sources of potential error, and these underline the importance of seemingly rather technical facts such as those concerning the camera attitude, and the precise time at which a photograph is taken. If the television receiver is maladjusted, the photograph may be stretched or compressed, and it is very difficult to allow for this particular distortion in rectification or gridding processes. Where identifiable surface features appear, the misfit can be distributed appropriately, but over ocean and overcast areas this is quite impossible. This seems to be one of the greatest single sources of error for which no adequate allowance can be made.

Providing that reception is perfect, and sufficient satellite information is available to permit the construction of an accurate grid, the primary problem is of a meteorological nature. Sometimes the centre or 'eye' of a hurricane is clearly visible as a dark spot in the centre of the cloudiness of the surrounding vortex, but on other occasions the eye may be obscured by high cloud, or it may even be absent altogether. If the eye cannot be seen it has to be assumed that the centre of the hurricane's characteristic disc of bright cloud is coincident with the circulation centre, which may not be a correct assumption.

In conclusion, it can be said that the location of weather features from a satellite photograph involves a wide range of considerations, including the nature of the satellite orbit, the calibration of both camera and receiver, and the characteristics of weather systems. For general purposes, locational errors of the order mentioned above are not serious—although in the specific context of the hurricane they may sometimes be critical, and constant efforts are being made to reduce the possible sources of error. Certainly locational problems are less acute where the angle of photography is designed to be a constant.

## Infra-red recordings

The meteorologist is not only interested in studying the atmosphere in so far that its condition is apparent in the visible wavelengths of the electro-magnetic spectrum, but also in the region of infra-red radiation. The energy which drives the circulation of the atmosphere is almost entirely derived from the sun, over 99 per cent arriving in wavelengths between 0·17 and 4·00 microns. Some of this is absorbed at the earth's surface, and by various constituents of the atmosphere, notably water vapour, carbon dioxide, and ozone,

24

whereas some is reflected back into Space. The balance varies from place to place, and from season to season, and the meteorologist needs to understand the heat budget of the atmosphere both in general and in detail. Solar energy within the atmosphere is the fuel which drives the general circulation, and its component systems such as the travelling depressions that make the weather in north-western Europe so interesting and variable. The satellite infra-red sensors are designed to investigate the radiation given off from various parts of the earth's surface and its atmosphere. The reasons for the choice of the various infra-red channels employed in the medium-resolution TIROS radiometer will be outlined later; suffice it to say at this stage that three different types of radiometer were tested during the experimental period, and these worked on the following principles:

### THE LOW RESOLUTION INFRA-RED RADIOMETER
This simply comprises two black and two white radiometers mounted on special extension arms whilst the satellite is in flight, thereby eliminating energy radiated or reflected from the satellite itself. The black sensors measure short-wave radiation from the sun and the earth, and the white sensors the long-wave radiation back into Space from the earth-atmosphere system. This is a low-resolution radiometer, its data being of interest primarily to students of the general heat balance, and of little use to those interested in individual weather systems.

### THE MEDIUM RESOLUTION INFRA-RED RADIOMETER
This is an extremely ingenious device, yielding information at the synoptic level of weather study. It involves alternate measurements from the earth and from Space, necessitating two viewing ports in the satellite, one in the baseplate and the other in the sidewall. Measurements are made in five different wavebands, this radiometer consisting of five similar sensors, each recording radiation from a particular earth or atmospheric source. In each, radiation waves from two directions 180° apart enter the spacecraft through the viewing ports (see Fig. 9) and are focused by a rectangular prism on to a second reflective surface. This, however, is only exposed to radiation from one direction at a time, a rotating 'chopper' cutting out the waves alternately from the other. Those that are allowed through are then passed through a selective filter, and a lens which concentrates those in the correct waveband on to a thermistor bolometer. Here an alternating electric current is generated, and the energy is

25

proportional to the difference in radiation from the two opposite directions. Since the Space sky radiates practically no infra-red waves, it acts as a very convenient zero-level reference for the radiation received from the earth.

Vast quantities of infra-red data have been obtained thus from the Space-orientated TIROS satellites, and have been employed in research studies despite the various problems attending their use. The field of view of each medium resolution scanner is about thirty

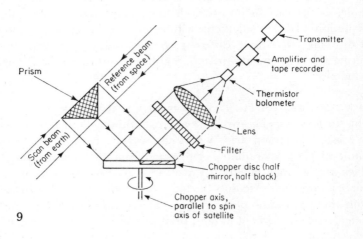

9

square miles when the observational angle is 90° with the earth's surface. When the observational position is oblique, as it is in the majority of cases, the area viewed is larger, shaped like a cut-off cone rather than a square. This complicates the interpretation of the data, which has not yet been employed as part of a routine investigatory procedure. Furthermore, the pattern of recordings made on a single orbital pass varies depending upon the attitude of the satellite and its spin about its axis. When the satellite is viewing the earth from a vertical position, the pattern of medium resolution infra-red recordings is circular, becoming elliptical, and finally an open U-shape as the horizons are approached and included. Fig. 10 illustrates the different patterns of observations recorded on any pass by a Space-orientated satellite.

Of the different patterns, it may seem that the circular or closed modes are most desirable, but this is not so in actual fact. It is difficult to locate the various data points unless the horizons are observed. These can be located mathematically and serve as map reference

26

points of a kind that the closed mode data cannot provide. It is not often possible to locate infra-red readings by physical landmarks, since these may not influence infra-red radiation as clearly as they influence visible radiation.

Despite these and other problems, however, radiometric information has already formed the basis of a number of interesting research studies, some of which are outlined later. In terms of future potential,

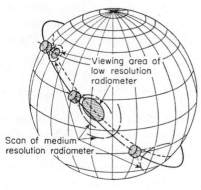

IO

this aspect of satellite meteorology is almost certainly more promising than cloud photography. It is possible, for example, that radiometers will enable meteorologists to compile vertical cross-sections of the atmosphere showing temperature variations from ground level to great heights. It is possible, too, that cloud distributions may be inferred just as accurately from infra-red data as from cloud photographs, with the added advantage that the altitudes of the upper surfaces of the clouds may be assessed quantitatively rather than in terms of their general visual appearances.

### THE HIGH-RESOLUTION INFRA-RED RADIOMETER

NIMBUS I was notable not only for its advanced camera systems, but also for its infra-red equipment. Compared with the resolution of the other two radiometers, that of the special NIMBUS model was very much more acute. Indeed, its resolution of 2–5 miles compared favourably with the resolution of the photographs taken by the wide-angled television cameras. Its primary purpose, however, was not day-time, but night-time observation. Between the wavelengths of about 3·4 and 4·2 microns, the atmosphere is relatively transparent unless water is present in a condensed form. This

27

is one of the so-called 'atmospheric window' wavebands. Infra-red observations in this waveband therefore record temperatures at the earth's surface if the sky is free from cloud, and cloud top temperatures where the sky is overcast. Thus the resulting temperature patterns should parallel closely the cloud patterns observed by photographic means, and 'cloud pictures' can be achieved even during the hours of darkness when visible radiation waves are absent, but surfaces continue to radiate within the infra-red region of the spectrum. It has been long suspected that diurnal rhythms of cloud growth and dissipation occur under certain weather conditions, but the impossibility of accurate observation of the clouds at night by visual means has prevented any earlier quantitative study of this phenomenon. The use of radar may be appropriate in a local setting, but it is only by satellite that a global investigation can be made.

At night the ocean surfaces are usually warmer than the adjacent land masses, since these cool more rapidly. In their turn, the land masses are usually warmer than the cloud tops. Since the amounts of radiation given off from these various surfaces are directly proportional to the fourth power of their temperatures, radiation in the middle of the night is greatest from the oceans and least from the tops of the clouds. By feeding the satellite signals into a radio facsimile recorder similar to that used for A.P.T. purposes, it is possible to obtain pictures that are closely, though not exactly, comparable to those received during the day from the camera systems, as can be seen from Plates 3a and 3b.

The high-resolution radiometer opens up many exciting new avenues of research, not only in meteorological research and in weather forecasting, but also in more purely geographical contexts.

### The operational weather satellite system

In February 1966 the experiments of the first six years of satellite meteorology finally bore fruit in the form of a regular observational network of satellites designed to observe the whole world daily, by television and A.P.T. means. Originally it was planned that the two satellites required at any time to give this kind of coverage should be known as TIROS TOSS—the TIROS Operational Satellite System. However, following the reorganisation of the various departments of the U.S. Department of Commerce, of which the U.S. Weather Bureau is one, into the Environmental Sciences Services Administration, the satellites have been designated by the name of ESSA (Environmental Survey Satellites) instead. ESSA 1 and 2 are 'cartwheel' type TIROS satellites orbiting at angles of 100° to the equator at altitudes of about 450 and 750 nautical miles respectively. One is equipped with television cameras (see Plate 2b), and the other with an A.P.T. camera system. It is intended that additional satellites will be launched as and when they are required to maintain one of either type in an operating condition. One provides sets of television pictures for the entire surface of the world at least once a day, and the other provides local information for forecasting centres in various countries.

Further NIMBUS and TIROS satellites of both types are planned for the future, both to maintain the flow of information, and to test new instruments and new orbits. Experimentation continues until the perfect system is evolved.

BIBLIOGRAPHY

Useful technical information has been published in the 'fact sheets' and 'press kits' prepared by the various organisations concerned with the development and deployment of the weather satellites, e.g. by the National Aeronautics and Space Administration of the U.S.A., who developed the NIMBUS system at the Goddard Space Flight Center, Greenbelt, Maryland, and the Radio Corporation of America who developed the TIROS system at their Astro-Electronic Products Division, Princeton, New Jersey. Useful articles of a general nature have included the following: M. Neiburger and H. Wexler, 'Weather Satellites', *Scientific American*, 41, 1960, 1; A. Schnapf, 'TIROS—the television and infra-red observation satellite', *Journal of the British Interplanetary Society*, **19**, 1964, 386; L.M. Mace and J.B. Jones, 'TIROS meteorological satellite: operational assists by TIROS', *Weatherwise*, **15**, 1962, 97; D.G. James and I.W. Pothecary, 'Some aspects of satellite meteorology', *Meteorological Magazine*, **94**, 1965, 193; M. Tepper and D.S. Johnson, 'Towards operational weather satellite systems', *Astronautics and Aeronautics*, (2), 1965, 16; R. Stampfl and H. Press, 'NIMBUS Spacecraft System', *Aerospace Engineering*, **21**, 1962, 16; D.S. Johnson, W. Ferguson Hall, and C.L. Bristor, 'NIMBUS data in operational meteorology', *Astronautics and Aerospace Engineering*, **1**(3), 1963, 52; P.E. Lehr, 'Methods of archiving, retrieving and utilising data acquired by TIROS meteorological satellites', *Bulletin of the American Meteorological Society*, **43**, 1962, 539. Various manuscripts presented as Meteorological Satellite Laboratory Reports by the U.S. Weather Bureau give valuable information on the technical aspects of handling satellite material. These include manuscripts by L.F. Hubert 'TIROS I—Camera attitude data,

29

analysis of location errors, and derivation of correction for calibration', M.S.L. Report No. 5, April 1961; M. Frankel and C.L. Bristor, *Perspective Locator Grids for TIROS Pictures*, M.S.L. Report No. 11, October 1962; and R.C. Doolittle, *Calibration of image distortion in TIROS wide angle photography*, M.S.L. Report No. 15, July 1963.

# 3 Analysing New Data

When new sources of data become available, new techniques are required to classify and analyse the facts that are obtained there-from. The analysis of weather satellite data may be considered under three headings, involving cloud photographs, the cloud charts that are compiled from them, and recordings made by the infra-red radio-meters.

## Cloud recognition

Ever since the first cloud photographs were obtained from TIROS I, much energy has been expended in the compilation of cloud cata-logues to aid the photo-interpreter who may be faced with a wide variety of weather situations within a single sequence of photo-graphs.

The new ability to see whole weather systems for the first time necessitated attention to be paid initially to *system recognition*, in-volving the study of typical cloud arrangements in atmospheric systems such as temperate depressions, hurricanes, and high pressure areas, to mention but a few. It soon became apparent as the work progressed that existing explanations in the form of physical models were frequently either inadequate or incomplete. The macro-patterns of clouds rarely conform to the theoretically expected patterns, suggesting that some of the models may require modification, but this cannot be attempted until careful empirical studies have been carried out.

Even the individual types of clouds themselves must be reclassified, since their appearances from satellite altitudes are often very differ-ent from those presented to the ground-based observer. In some cases the individual cloudlets visible from the ground cannot be seen on a satellite photograph since the resolution is too coarse. On the other hand, sheets of stratiform cloud that appear structureless and amorphous viewed from the ground, possess clear structural features that can be seen on a smaller scale.

The first comprehensive cloud catalogue compiled from satellite photographs was produced by J.H. Conover in 1962 and modified and brought up to date in 1963. This will, no doubt, be succeeded by more highly detailed catalogues as clearer photographs become available, but the general principles by which clouds may be recognised have been laid down satisfactorily, and will be modified little in the foreseeable future.

Conover undertook an exhaustive study comparing photographs from the TIROS satellites with others of the same areas of cloud as seen from the ground and from reconnaissance aircraft. He listed six different characteristics that must be taken into account in any such study, namely the brightness, texture, structure, shape or form, pattern, and dimensions of the clouds and cloud systems. These headings may be adopted here as useful systematic bases for an introduction to the main problems of cloud recognition.

CLOUD BRIGHTNESS

Of the six characteristics, this is probably the most difficult to investigate, since brightness depends not only upon meteorological variables, but also on mechanical and photographic factors. The age of the television camera, for example, is known to affect picture quality, and the brightness scale. The development process of the 35 mm photographs in the dark room can also affect the absolute range of tone.

Brightness, moreover, may not remain constant across a single sequence of photographs even if the same types of clouds recur. The amount of light that is reflected back into Space from cloud surfaces depends not only upon the nature of those surfaces themselves, but also on the relative position of the sun. It has been shown that illumination on a horizontal surface near sea-level, under cloudless conditions and with a low water vapour content in the atmosphere, increases fourfold as the angle of incidence of the sun's rays rises from 20° to 90°. Assuming that a similar increase may be expected where the surface is a fairly smooth sheet of cloud, a single cloud type obviously cannot be characterised by a constant brightness level. Sometimes sunlight reflected from the sea or a lake surface is intercepted by a satellite and appears on the photographs as a diffuse area of intense brightness, as shown by Plate 7f. 'Sun-glint' may be misinterpreted as cloudiness unless care is taken, especially when the area of sun-glint overlaps the edge of a stratiform cloud mass, making the definition of the cloud boundary a difficult task.

Finally, turning to the factors relating brightness to the nature of the actual clouds themselves, it has been shown that both the depth of cloud and the nature of the cloud constituents must be considered. The albedo, or reflectivity, of clouds increases rapidly with depth and reaches a maximum when they are only 200 metres deep provided that the cloud droplets are large. Where the droplets are small in size, brightness increases less rapidly with depth, and may not reach the maximum until the cloud depths are more than twice that figure.

With all these possible sources of variability in cloud brightness to be borne in mind it may well be asked whether this is a feature that can be used at all in cloud interpretation. To this, the answer is a definite 'yes', provided that brightness is assessed in each photograph individually, and comparisons between photographs of widely separated areas, or those taken at different times of the day in one locality, or from different stages in the life of one satellite, are all avoided. In cyclone cloud systems the relationship between cloud brightness and cloud depth is probably quite close; so, it seems, may be the relationship between the brightest areas and those of active precipitation. The frontal cloudiness associated with a temperate depression is frequently banded in tone, with broad streaks of white embedded in the grey. The whiter bands, probably corresponding to areas of deeper cloud, with higher types overlying nimbo-stratus or strato-cumulus, are those from which rain is most likely to fall, a suggestion at least partially confirmed by simultaneous radar observations of precipitation.

Comparisons have also shown that water clouds appear brighter than ice crystal clouds of similar thickness under similar conditions of illumination. Cirrus and cirro-stratus clouds, for example, are frequently translucent when they occur alone, and may be visible only when they occur against a dark background. A thin sheet of stratus is usually visible as a predominantly grey cloud veil.

CLOUD TEXTURE
This is a good indicator of cloud type: whether the cloudiness is diffuse or complete, variegated or smooth in appearance.

The most difficult clouds to spot on satellite photographs are the very thin, high altitude types, and their developing presence often has to be deduced from an apparent loss of definition of terrestrial features where the same area is re-photographed on successive orbits.

When cirriform clouds can be seen, they usually appear in a haphazard, fibrous form, or alternatively, as a smooth translucent area of cloud blown out in a feathery fashion around its margins. An excellent example of the latter smoother variety is afforded by the high shield of cirriform cloudiness which is often found overlying a hurricane, its translucency permitting the denser, deeper cloudiness of the low-level storm beneath to be seen quite clearly.

It is this translucency which helps to distinguish it from low-level stratus on those occasions when the texture is not an adequate criterion. On many occasions, however, the very high clouds are fibrous and streaky in appearance, quite unlike the smoothly homogeneous stratus or fog, which, furthermore, tends to conform itself to the pattern of land and sea. Some excellent photographs have shown sea fog in the English Channel with quite abrupt edges along the coasts of Southern England and Northern France, and others have portrayed low stratus blanketing the warmer winter waters around the west coast of Norway, contrasting with the cloud-free, snow-covered peninsula. (See Plate 4a.)

Confusion is much more likely to occur between small scattered pockets of fog in hilly terrain, and scattered cumuliform cloudiness of the kind that is normally associated with fair summer weather in the British Isles. Normally, however, the photo-analyst will have a recent synoptic weather chart near at hand, even if he is dealing with a region from which few local weather reports are available. Interpretation rarely has to be attempted in the complete absence of weather data from conventional sources, although this may happen in many ocean areas. Cloud photographs will never entirely replace ground-based observations of the weather; the one investigation supplements the other, providing two different perspectives of the same thing. Individual satellite photographs may show some very complicated patterns of cloudiness, but these rarely have to be interpreted completely on their own merits. The distinct possibility of confusing stratus or sea-fog with other varieties of low stratiform clouds can be eliminated often by reference to the prevalent pressure pattern, and, indeed by reference to the organisation of cloudiness on a larger scale.

VERTICAL CLOUD STRUCTURE

It is sometimes helpful to note indications of the structure of the clouds in the vertical plane. Even with the NIMBUS or 'cartwheel' TIROS systems, the only areas of cloud that are really viewed in the vertical are those around the sub-points of the cameras. Obliqueness,

34

in any satellite photograph, increases away from these points, as it does in all aerial photographs, and it is accentuated by the curvature of the earth. Sometimes, therefore, the side walls of clouds may be visible, and help to distinguish the deeper clouds from the shallow. Of equal significance are the shadows cast by the tall clouds. These have been noted along depression fronts, the tall clouds building upwards through a stratiform overcast as the warm sector air is lifted from the ground by the undercutting cold sector air, increasing instability in what is likely to be an already unstable air mass. From a satellite, the frontal cloud often appears as a roughened surface, especially when the depression is actively occluding, and the warm sector air is being forced upwards.

## THE FORM OF CLOUD ELEMENTS

Whereas texture is a useful criterion in the identification of stratiform cloud types, the form of small cloud elements is more significant when cumuliform clouds prevail.

The cycle of cloud development on a warm anticyclonic day in summer will be familiar to most: a clear blue sky over land in the early morning tends to become dotted with small shallow cumulus as the morning progresses, and these often continue to grow in the afternoon, not only laterally, but vertically too, until the sky may be almost covered with deep clouds. Some of these develop more than others until they become towering cumulo-congesti or even cumulo-nimbi. As the land cools in the late afternoon and evening, the clouds break up and dissipate, along with or without convectional rain storms, clearing the sky again at the end of the diurnal cycle. Since the present weather satellites cannot see fine detail, the morning cloudiness may be difficult to observe. Summer anticyclonic cumulus grows over land rather than over the sea, and coastlines may appear as definite as usual. The only suggestion that clouds may be present may be an unusually light greyness of the land. By afternoon, however, the enlarged cumuli become visible, and the larger thunderclouds stand out as very bright cloud elements, which may cast long shadows if the sun is not too high in the sky.

In the tropics, convective activity is a daily phenomenon, and the photo-analyst is frequently called upon to distinguish thunderclouds from less well-developed cloudiness. (See Plate 7e.) From the ground, majestic cumulo-nimbi are often very distinctive, with their high solid towers capped with cirriform streamers blowing downwind in the form of flattened anvil tops, the pillars themselves probably tilting forwards under the influence of the stronger winds aloft. From the satellite, the form is equally distinctive. A tail of dull grey, possibly translucent cirrus, extends away from the bright disc of the tower cloud, the whole appearance being reminiscent of a carrot. This is an extremely characteristic cloud form, and, to the interpreter, tells not only of the prevailing thundery conditions, but also of the direction of wind flow at altitudes of 30,000 feet and more, the tail of cirrus pointing in a downwind direction.

### CLOUD PATTERNS

If the nature of some cloud types is still in doubt after the foregoing criteria have all been considered, then the *patterns* of the individual cloud elements may be helpful. A great deal of research has already been carried out from this viewpoint, investigating the relationships between cloud patterns and the associated pressure distributions. Many of the observed cloud patterns conform to existing atmospheric models, but a number of unexpected patterns have been discovered by the satellites. Over ocean areas, for example, a number of very curious cloud patterns, whose presence had passed unnoticed from surface observations, have been brought to light. Some of these patterns, which frequent the central Pacific and southern Indian Oceans in particular, will be described in detail in Chapter 7, along with other clouds whose formation seems to be related to the nature of the underlying surface.

One pattern may be discussed in detail now, namely that associated with a jet stream in the upper troposphere—this may help the interpreter to distinguish between strong cirriform cloudiness and lower clouds of a stratiform type. Jet streams are rapid rivers of air meandering around the world through comparatively stagnant air at high altitudes. They are good examples of so-called 'thermal' winds, generated by marked horizontal temperature contrasts in neighbouring air masses in the lower atmosphere. They are characteristically found, therefore, above the major 'fronts' that mark the boundaries between air masses of polar or tropical origins. Perhaps the best developed is the polar frontal jet stream, which meanders around the northern hemisphere in middle latitudes, associated with the boundary along which most of the depressions of the North Atlantic and North Pacific are generated and tend to move. Since the jets are high level winds, the clouds associated with them are usually thin, cirriform clouds. Occasionally, however, they may be quite dense, and it is then that their unique patterns may distinguish them from lower bands of clouds.

The jet stream cirrus either organises itself as a number of broken strap-like bands of cloud, or in a ladder-like pattern which results from a rather curious balance of forces occurring in the zone of the jet. The primary cause of movement within the atmosphere is the horizontal variability of atmospheric pressure, and 'wind flow' is the result. Different surfaces respond differently to radiative warming, and relative expansion and contraction of the overlying air leads to the development of horizontal pressure gradients. Air tends to move from high to low pressure to neutralise the pressure differences. Since the earth is a rotating body, however, moving air suffers

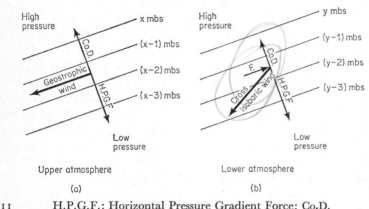

Upper atmosphere         Lower atmosphere

(a)               (b)

11        H.P.G.F.: Horizontal Pressure Gradient Force; Co.D.
Coriolis Deflection; F.: Friction Force

an apparent deflection to the right in the northern hemisphere, and to the left south of the equator. The horizontal magnitude of this, the so-called Coriolis deflection, increases from the equator to the poles, and is proportional to the wind speed. In the upper atmosphere, the pressure gradient force and the Coriolis deflection tend to balance, and winds blow parallel to the isobars, and not perpendicularly across them as the case would be if the earth were non-rotating. In the lower atmosphere, friction reduces the wind speed, and indirectly, therefore, the amount of the Coriolis deflection, so that air does cross the isobars, albeit at a low angle. These differences are summarised in Fig. 11.

At the jet stream altitudes, wind flow along the isobars tends to perpetuate the existing pressure gradients, confining the motion to isobaric channels. Along the cores of the jet streams, however, much steeper pressure gradients are encountered, and wind speeds of 200 m.p.h. or more may be recorded. The air must accelerate as it passes through the jet stream's entrance zone. The rapid steepening of the pressure gradient on approaching the core zone disturbs the balance between the pressure gradient and the Coriolis deflection, causing the motion to become sub-geostrophic or, should the isobars be curved, sub-gradient. The air achieves the necessary acceleration by moving across the isobars in the direction of lower pressure. In the core zone the geostrophic or gradient balance tends to be re-established, and the cloudiness appears as a long sinuous streak from satellite altitudes. When lower cloud is present beneath it, the line of the jet can often be inferred from long shadows cast by the streaks of cirrus.

In the exit zone of the jet stream the flow must decelerate and this is achieved by movement across the isobars towards *higher* pressure, which acts as a brake since work must be done against the pressure gradient force. The flow is then 'supergradient' or super-geostrophic. It must be stressed that the component of flow directed along the isobars is still greatly in excess of that across them. The latter is quite significant, though, because of the circulations it may initiate in the vertical, which can have appreciable effects on the pattern of rainfall. Moreover, the upper-tropospheric convergence on the equatorwards side of the jet contributes notably to the strengthening of the subtropical anticyclones at that level, in a pro-cess of 'dynamic anticyclogenesis'. The high speeds in the jet stream core are attributable not only to the strong pressure gradients, but also to the fact that the velocity in geostrophic flow is inversely pro-portional to the density of the air, which is here only about one-quarter of the value attained at sea level.

The distinctive patterns of jet stream cloudiness in the entry and exit zones are ladder-like in plan. The poleward margin of the exit zone pattern for example, is comprised of a more or less continuous streak of dense cirrus, which is thought to mark the main stream of the jet, the central axis of its flow. Fronds of cirriform clouds fan out in the direction of the supergradient wind, and tend to coalesce along a line parallel to the central axis. This 'ladder' pattern seems to be quite characteristic of a supergradient situation, and can usually be identified even when it is underlain by lower cloudiness, perhaps of a frontal nature, since the high cirrus again casts a shadow on the cloud deck below.

### THE SIGNIFICANCE OF SIZE

The final criterion Conover used in the interpretation of cloud photo-graphs involved the dimensions of the various patterns and forms, helping to relate them to known atmospheric systems of air flow. An interesting fact which has emerged from long and careful acquain-

38

tance with satellite photographs is that certain arrangements of clouds tend to be repeated across a wide range of scales. For example, spiral patterns of stratiform clouds may be organised across an area only a few miles in diameter, or a region hundreds of miles wide. Plate 4b illustrates a small cloud spiral in close proximity to the organised cloudiness associated with a similar, but much larger vortex whose centre is off the photograph. Whether or not similar arrangements at different scales result from the operation of similar processes is a difficult question to answer with confidence, although the likelihood is that this is so. It is important to remember, however, that bands of stratiform cloudiness at one scale may be confused with lines of cumuli at another unless care is taken, and it could be that similar patterns at different scales may sometimes consist of different cloud types, whether or not the causes of the circulations are the same.

## The compilation of nephanalyses

The correct interpretation of satellite cloud photographs is not only important in meteorological research, but also in daily weather fore-casting. At an early stage in the weather satellite programme it was found that the photographs could not be transmitted from the C.D.A. stations to forecasting offices by landline without a considerable loss of definition. It was deemed necessary, therefore, to employ skilled photo-interpreters at the C.D.A. stations themselves, to construct cloud maps from the photographs so that their salient features might be shown in a way that would not suffer unduly from a loss of clarity. These maps or charts were sent abroad to the forecasting offices of other nations such as the United Kingdom, via a radio facsimile network which is being retained despite the success of A.P.T. photo-graphy: A.P.T. satellites provide a restricted number of pictures of local weather conditions, whereas the cloud charts portray the weather over a much wider area, and are particularly valuable in forecasting highly mobile weather situations.

The compilation of cloud charts at the C.D.A. stations is also advantageous in that there is a less urgent need for the professional weather forecaster to acquire a highly developed skill in photo-interpretation. The television photographs, like any aerial photo-graphs, portray actual situations in all their detail, and some simplification is necessary if they are to be used in current forecasting procedures. The technical name that has been given to the cloud chart is 'nephanalysis' a term that has long been used by meteor-ologists to denote the investigation of large-scale patterns, types and distributions of clouds, but one which has now acquired this much more specific meaning. The purpose of the satellite nephanalysis is to represent in symbol form the predominant cloud types viewed by the satellite, to show the orientation of medium and large-scale cloud bands, and to suggest synoptic interpretations of the clouds in terms of atmospheric pressure patterns.

Although the whole business of nephanalysis construction is constantly being modified and brought up to date as a result of improved photo-resolution and increasing skill in photo-interpretation, a basic scheme can be outlined, which was in use at the end of 1965, and whose framework seems sufficiently well proven to ensure that it will continue to be used for some time to come. Obviously an element of subjectivity is involved in compiling nephanalyses, and much less detail is shown than in the original photographs, but these cloud charts are currently still one of the most useful forms of weather satellite data employed routinely by the main short-term forecasting centres of the world.

Fig. 12 lists the information that can be shown on a nephanalysis. It is instructive to examine this information in more detail at this stage, to illustrate the principles that are involved, and the problems that are associated with them.

*Cloud Element.* This is the smallest distinguishable unit in a cloud mass or cloud pattern as seen by a weather satellite. The term is used especially in connection with cumuliform clouds.

*Cloud Mass.* This is an identifiable patch of cloud elements. Generally speaking, it must be equal to, or greater than, two degrees square of latitude in size, and within the patch the actual cloud itself should occupy at least 80 per cent of the total area.

A *Cloud Pattern* is a distinctive organisation of cloud elements, groups of elements, or cloud masses. It was noted earlier that patterns appear in satellite photographs across a wide range of scale, and a subdivision is conventionally made between micro- (small-scale), meso- (medium-scale), and macro-scale (large-scale) patterns.

A *Cloud System* consists of the cloudiness produced by, or associated with, the dynamics of any atmospheric pressure system; for example, a tropical storm, an anticyclone, or an extratropical depression. One of the basic tenets of nephanalysis compilation is the fact that each

40

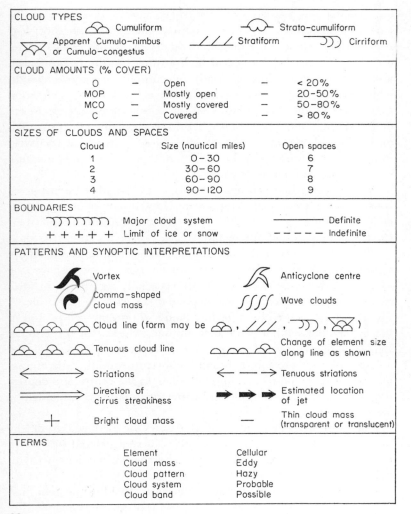

| CLOUD TYPES | | | |
|---|---|---|---|
| ⌒⌒ Cumuliform | | ⌒⌒⌒ Strato-cumuliform | |
| Apparent Cumulo-nimbus or Cumulo-congestus | ⁄⁄⁄ Stratiform | ͡))) Cirriform | |

| CLOUD AMOUNTS (% COVER) | | | |
|---|---|---|---|
| O | — | Open | — < 20% |
| MOP | — | Mostly open | — 20-50% |
| MCO | — | Mostly covered | — 50-80% |
| C | — | Covered | — > 80% |

| SIZES OF CLOUDS AND SPACES | | |
|---|---|---|
| Cloud | Size (nautical miles) | Open spaces |
| 1 | 0-30 | 6 |
| 2 | 30-60 | 7 |
| 3 | 60-90 | 8 |
| 4 | 90-120 | 9 |

| BOUNDARIES | | |
|---|---|---|
| ͡)͡)͡)͡)͡)͡) Major cloud system | ———— Definite | |
| + + + + + Limit of ice or snow | — — — — — Indefinite | |

PATTERNS AND SYNOPTIC INTERPRETATIONS

| | | | |
|---|---|---|---|
| 🦅 Vortex | | 𝒜 Anticyclone centre | |
| 𝒫 Comma-shaped cloud mass | | ∫∫∫∫ Wave clouds | |
| ⌒⌒ ⌒⌒ ⌒⌒ Cloud line (form may be ⌒⌒ , ⁄⁄⁄ , ͡)) , ⌒⌒ ) | | | |
| ⌒⌒ ⌒⌒ ⌒⌒ Tenuous cloud line | | ⌒⌒⌒ ⌒⌒ Change of element size along line as shown | |
| ←——→ Striations | | ←— —→ Tenuous striations | |
| ══⟶ Direction of cirrus streakiness | | ➡ ➡ ➡ Estimated location of jet | |
| ╅ Bright cloud mass | | — Thin cloud mass (transparent or translucent) | |

| TERMS | | |
|---|---|---|
| | Element | Cellular |
| | Cloud mass | Eddy |
| | Cloud pattern | Hazy |
| | Cloud system | Probable |
| | Cloud band | Possible |

12

distinctive system of clouds can usually be related to a definite circulatory system in the atmosphere.

*Cloud Band.* A cloud band is really a special kind of cloud pattern, being one in which the long axis of cloudiness exceeds the width by a ratio of at least four to one. This formation may consist entirely of cloud, or may include some clear sky; it may be either straight or curved in plan.

From the earliest days four main cloud types have been portrayed

41

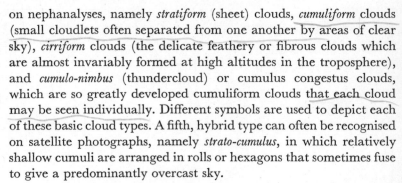

on nephanalyses, namely *stratiform* (sheet) clouds, *cumuliform* clouds (small cloudlets often separated from one another by areas of clear sky), *cirriform* clouds (the delicate feathery or fibrous clouds which are almost invariably formed at high altitudes in the troposphere), and *cumulo-nimbus* (thundercloud) or cumulus congestus clouds, which are so greatly developed cumuliform clouds that each cloud may be seen individually. Different symbols are used to depict each of these basic cloud types. A fifth, hybrid type can often be recognised on satellite photographs, namely *strato-cumulus*, in which relatively shallow cumuli are arranged in rolls or hexagons that sometimes fuse to give a predominantly overcast sky.

The *boundaries* between one cloud type and another often possess considerable meteorological significance, and are represented graphically according to their kind (frontal or non-frontal) and their clarity (definite, indefinite or indistinct).

Whilst the clouds in and around depressions and anticyclones are significant indicators of wind flow and the humidity of the air, the *positions of the centres of circulation* are especially significant in forecasting, and are shown on the nephanalyses whenever possible. A similar symbol is used both for high and low pressure centres but in the former the symbol is an open outline, whereas in the latter a solid symbol is employed instead. The difference reflects the fact that a centre of high pressure is usually related to subsiding, diverging, and relatively cloud-free conditions, whereas the centre of a depression is marked by converging and rising air usually accompanied by an area of denser cloudiness.

Upper-air arrangements can sometimes be deduced from the photographs, especially in the vicinity of a well defined jet stream flow, and the positions and directions of the various jets are symbolised on the cloud charts.

The steady improvement that has been achieved in the definition of weather satellite photographs has been reflected in the amount of detailed information portrayed by nephanalyses. There are few of the cloud characteristics outlined above that cannot now be classified in greater detail than at first. For example, the cloud bands are themselves frequently composed of a number of cloud *lines*, whose individual cloud elements, whether linked or separate, are visible. Generally a line such as this is only one cloud element in width, whereas its length may be quite considerable. Recent nephanalyses have been designed to show the direction of the alignment, the type or types of cloud elements involved, and changes in the size of the elements along the cloud lines. The forecaster may be able to infer

42

from these details changes in humidity and the strength of the wind, and, perhaps, the direction of wind shear, which is the direction of the maximum change in wind speed with height above the ground. This last parameter helps to indicate the relationship between high and low level pressure patterns within the troposphere. Lee-wave clouds, comprised of lines of cloudiness roughly parallel to one another, can often be recognised on the downwind sides of mountain chains, and humidity and wind inferences can be drawn from these particular cloud lines also.

Although the main purpose of a nephanalysis is to portray the significant features of the clouds, certain non-meteorological phenomena are recorded as a matter of routine, and ice and snow features are the most prominent examples. A snow line is shown where clouds are thin or absent, and the frozen surfaces can be delimited with confidence. Problems often arise when one attempts to distinguish a snow-covered lowland from a patch of sea-ice, although geographical locator grids and coastline keys may be helpful then. A more serious problem involves the similarity in appearance between snow and ice on the one hand, and cloudiness on the other; this problem will discussed in Chapter 9.

*Marginal information.* Thus a wealth of information concerning both cloud and terrain features may be depicted within the actual map area of the nephanalysis, which is based upon a selected conventional projection. In addition, explanatory comments are often added around the map margins. The exact geographical co-ordinates of a centre of high or low pressure may be extremely important from a forecasting point of view, especially if the low pressure system is deep and active, and locational information is given in the map margin in degrees and minutes of latitude and longitude. Other pithy, yet informative marginal remarks may concern, for example, the various cellular patterns of cumuliform or strato-cumuliform cloud elements. The more common patterns are the 'open' and the 'closed': in the former, the clouds are doughnut-shaped, with clear centres; in the latter, solid discs of cloud are separated from one another by a lattice of cloud-free interstices. Suffice it to say at this stage that these different modes indicate differences in atmospheric stability, another variable in which the short-term forecaster has a keen interest.

It is not difficult to imagine, furthermore, that a fairly uniform flow of air in the lower atmosphere must be more or less disturbed as it passes over and around abrupt surface physical features, such

43

as isolated mountains or archipelagos. Frequently, localised disturbances result in the appearance, in plan, of curious spiraliform cloud patterns, which comprise visible indicators of atmospheric eddies. These again afford valuable clues to local weather conditions, and their presence is recorded, along with their co-ordinates, in the margins of the charts.

Finally, the existence of 'hazy' conditions are noted when relief features that could be seen clearly on a previous pass are no longer visible with the same clarity. The cause may be either the early development of high level cirrus cloudiness, or low level mist and fog; once again, the weather forecaster may be afforded a useful clue concerning weather development.

In conclusion, of course, it must be admitted that there are many occasions on which it is difficult to interpret with complete confidence the features portrayed by the satellite photographs. It is not always easy to classify an area of cloud, or to say exactly where the boundary should be drawn between cloudy and cloud free skies, or between ice and snow, and cloud. The precise location of a depression centre may be difficult to determine, or, in fact, whether an apparently spiral cloud system is related to an atmospheric vortex or not. Photo-interpretation necessitates an honest approach; hence the frequency with which charted features are described as only 'possible' or 'probable'. The photo-interpreter, by convention, discribes his suggestions as 'possibly' correct when an unusual feature is present, or when the available synoptic analyses based on conventional meteorological observations seem to contradict them. His suggestions are 'probably' correct when only a part of a cloud pattern or system is visible within the area viewed on a single satellite pass but its appearance is typical, or when the cloudiness is distorted by its situation near the horizon, but the interpretation of it can be corroborated by the evidence of photographs of the same area, or a closely adjacent one, taken on a previous orbit.

### Radiation data

Since the information that has been received from the medium- and high-resolution sensors is more precise than that from the less sophisticated low-resolution sensor, attention may be focused solely on those first two named. Despite the fact that weather forecasters have not yet been able to use radiation data in the course of their daily investigations, preliminary research work has suggested that its future potential is very great.

Table 3 (p. 130) details the different wavelengths investigated by the medium-resolution radiometer as employed in several of the TIROS satellites. The wavelengths were chosen for the following reasons:

*Channel 1* measures the energy which is absorbed by the water vapour component of the atmosphere, the amount of this gas depending partly on the temperature of the air, since warmer air is able to hold much more water in its gaseous form than colder air can. In TIROS VII Channel 1 recorded in the wave-band from 14·5–15·5 μ, to give a measure of the energy radiated by carbon dioxide. (See. pp. 51–4.)

*Channel 2.* This most important channel, extending from 8–12μ, crosses the broadest 'atmospheric window'. In this region of the electromagnetic spectrum, cloudless portions of the atmosphere are transparent to radiation, whereas even a thin veil of cloud is opaque. Hence, the radiation measured by the satellite in this waveband relates to the temperature of the ground surface itself in cloudless areas, but to the temperatures of the upper surfaces of the clouds where these are present. Although this 'window' occupies a mere fraction of the infra-red segment of the spectrum, the variations in the radiation from the earth and its atmosphere towards Space are very largely due to variations in radiation escaping through it. Cloud cover is therefore a most important factor in the heat budget of the earth, and more research has been based on data from Channel 2 than on that from any other. Radiation patterns derived from this channel serve as quite acceptable cloud maps, and can be interpreted separately, or alongside the cloud photographs themselves, having an advantage over the latter in that the heights of the clouds can be deduced in quantitative terms.

*Channel 3* is another broad channel, this time measuring the energy of *reflected* solar radiation, which, when expressed as a percentage of the incoming radiation reaching a cloud or terrestrial surface, is known as the 'albedo'. Some surfaces reflect more efficiently than others, but are warmed less as a result. Generally speaking, light-coloured surfaces reflect more efficiently than darker ones, so that the surfaces of ice or snow, and clouds may possess albedos rising as high as 80 per cent. Desert areas, with an average albedo of about 25 per cent are, by comparison, the most highly reflective snow-free land surfaces, and most land and water surfaces reflect only between 3 per cent and 15 per cent of the sunlight energy falling upon them. It is possible for water surfaces to reflect much more efficiently than this, but only if the sun is low in the sky and the surface is not unduly

45

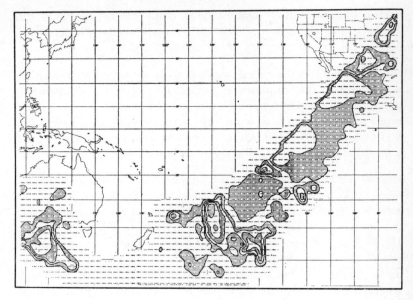

13a

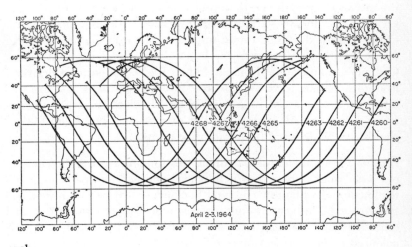

13b

ruffled by waves. The albedo channel is designed to measure over 99 per cent of all the back-scattered and reflected sunshine from the surface and the atmosphere of the earth.

*Channel 4.* This is the broadest channel, extending from 7–30μ, measuring the total infra-red radiation given off from the earth-

46

atmosphere system. It covers those portions of the spectrum in which energy is given off from water vapour and carbon dioxide and ozone, the three most important gases in heat budget studies.

*Channel 5.* This is a narrow channel, extending from $0 \cdot 55$–$0 \cdot 75\mu$, and therefore measuring radiation within the waveband of visible light energy. Its purpose is for reference, to assist in the locating of radiometer data by affording a comparison with cloud photographs.

When the radiation data from each of these five channels are received by a C.D.A. station, they are fed into an electronic computer which compiles and prints out a map for each week's observations. A squared grid is superimposed upon this accumulated information, and an average radiation value is calculated for each grid square. Catalogues of data processed thus are available for certain members of the TIROS family, and transparent overlay grids are provided for the convenience of the researcher. Fig. 13a illustrates this mode of presentation. Using a catalogue of this kind, it is a simple task to study regional variations in infra-red radiation, either for the weekly periods themselves, or for longer seasons. Fig. 13b illustrates the coverage provided by TIROS VII in terms of the satellite orbits for which infra-red data were obtained.

BIBLIOGRAPHY
Photoanalysis is discussed by J.H. Conover in *Cloud Interpretation from Satellite Altitudes*, Air Force Cambridge Research Laboratories Research Note 81, 1962, and 'The interpretation of cloud pictures from the TIROS meteorological satellite', *Journal of the Society of Motion Picture and Television Engineers*, **71**, 1962, 21. See also *The Use of Satellite Pictures in Weather Analysis and Forecasting*, Technical Note No. 75, World Meteorological Organisation, 1966.
A number of articles dealing with cloud interpretation across a wide range of scales have been published in *Rocket and Satellite Meteorology* edited by H. Wexler and J.E. Caskey, this being the report of the proceedings of the first International Symposium on Rocket and Satellite Meteorology, Washington DC 1962, and published by North-Holland Publishing Company, Amsterdam 1963. This also includes a useful section on meteorological satellite radiation studies.
Jet stream articles have included those by V.J. Oliver, R.K. Anderson and E.W. Ferguson, 'Some examples of the detection of jet streams from TIROS photographs', *Monthly Weather Review*, **92**,

1964, 441; and L.F. Whitney, A. Timchalk and T.I. Gray, 'On locating jet streams from TIROS photographs', *Monthly Weather Review*, **94** 1966, 127. For general jet stream theory the reader's attention is drawn especially to H. Riehl *et al.*, 'Forecasting in middle latitudes', *Meteorological Monographs*, **1**, 1952; and V.J. Schaefer, 'Cloud forms of the jet stream', *Tellus*, **5**, 1953, 27. E.R. Reiter, *Jet Stream Meteorology*, Chicago, 1963, is a comprehensive text.

# PART TWO

# New Light on Old Problems

INTRODUCTION

# Satellite Contributions to our Knowledge of the Atmosphere

The geographer is often called upon to relate, either consciously or subconsciously, events and distributions in his own immediate locality to those that are characteristic of very much larger regions, even to those of the world as a whole. Thus the economic geographer, interested primarily perhaps in local patterns, needs to know and understand the way in which these patterns affect, and are affected by, the larger scale patterns into which they fit. Cause-and-effect relationships connect local details, through a whole hierarchy of stages, to the macro-structure of the world economy itself. Similarly, the geomorphologist, who may begin by studying on a small scale the evidences of changes in erosional base-levels in his own chosen local region, may well wish at a later date to relate the succession of changes he has found there to those that other workers have found in the rest of Europe, or in even larger regions.

It is particularly important to appreciate relationships between the small-scale and the large when studying the weather. National boundaries and different geological outcrops cause economic and geomorphological discontinuities to abound, and may permit the localisation of one's attention in these fields to be justified far more easily than the localisation of a study in the atmosphere, in which static, clearly defined boundaries do not occur. The student of the weather deals with a continuum that obeys the laws of fluid motion, and he must be forced ultimately to understand a broad perspective even if his primary interests are in micro-climatic or micro-meteorological fields. Both the research worker and the local weather fore-caster are forced to examine variations in hemispheric patterns if they wish to find the 'ultimate' explanations of local weather anomalies. This central section of the book seeks to explain some of the contributions that weather satellites have been able to make already towards a fuller knowledge and understanding of atmospheric phenomena ranging from the local to the world-wide, from the meteorological aspects of the weather to the study of climate.

Meteorology is essentially a mathematical and physical science. Its emphasis is upon the instantaneous, upon the nature and the causes of weather. Climatology, on the other hand, as behoves its importance within the geographical sciences, is more concerned with averages, and concentrates most of its attention upon the plane of the horizontal. Mathematical and physical considerations are still important, but as generalities rather than precise formulations for individual cases. Although no attempt has been made in the chapters that follow to separate meteorological from climatological discussion, a progression has been made from the large-scale to the small. This tends to be the reverse of the usual research approach, but it lends itself better to a coherent logical account, and is, furthermore, the pattern adopted by many textbooks, with which the reader may like to compare the information outlined here.

Chapter 4 seeks to outline the planetary atmospheric circulation, and the contributions that weather satellites have been able to make towards our understanding of it. Chapters 5 and 6 discuss weather systems in two of the major climatic zones of the world, namely the tropics and the temperate mid-latitudinal regions. Little can be said yet concerning polar weather, since few satellites have orbited at sufficiently high angles to the equator for much additional data to be derived from the areas about the poles. Furthermore the difficulty with which cloud can be distinguished from ice and snow lowers the utility of the available photographs. Some of the surface geographical phenomena within the Arctic and Antarctic regions have been studied more profitably than the weather, and Chapter 9 is devoted entirely to a description of the earth's surface as seen from Space. Chapter 7 discusses some of the local variations in weather that the satellites have been able to detect; the future is bright with promise here, since the instruments of observation will become increasingly refined, and the improvements in resolution will permit even more detailed studies to be made. Chapter 8 is devoted to the contributions that have been made by satellites to weather forecasting.

50

# 4 The General Circulation of the Atmosphere

## Stratospheric patterns

Although the temperature of the atmosphere decreases generally with height to the level of the tropopause, it tends to remain steady in the stratosphere above. Within the troposphere convection is a dominant meteorological process, involving the expansion and cooling of bubbles of warm air that rise from the heated surfaces of the earth, and the compression and warming of the air that sinks to take their place. At the higher level of the stratosphere, an almost perfect balance exists between outgoing radiation and loss of heat, and the absorption of incoming heat energy from the sun. The tropopause, the boundary plane between the two, changes in altitude from the equator to the poles, since the surface of the earth is more effectively heated in low latitudes and convective activity is more powerful there. The tropopause consists therefore of an inclined plane, some eleven miles high within the tropics, but only about five miles high over the poles.

The tropopause is a very significant entity in meteorology in that it separates the lowest layer of the atmosphere, that within which the weather systems that affect the surface are contained, from a layer whose internal pressure and temperature variations are much more exclusively related to seasonal changes in the relative positions of the earth and the sun. Since the patterns within the stratosphere are much simpler, and change in a more straightforward way than those in the troposphere, it is convenient to describe stratospheric variations as deduced from satellite infra-red investigations as an introduction to the major problems of the general circulation.

In TIROS VII, one of the five medium-resolution infra-red radiometers measured in the waveband from 14·8–15·5μ. Within this waveband most of the radiation is received from the carbon dioxide content of the atmosphere. By removing from the satellite data the radiation contributed by carbon dioxide above and below the stratosphere, radiation patterns can be obtained for the stratosphere alone, whose temperatures are steady from 15–35 km above the earth's surface. TIROS VII orbited at 58° to the equator, and supplied a continuous flow of infra-red recordings for a period of about 9 months in 1963 and 1964 encircling the earth between the latitude of 65° North and 65° South. Maps were compiled to trace the changes that occurred in stratospheric temperature patterns from season to season as first one pole and then the other was inclined towards the sun. In the stratosphere pressure patterns coincide closely with those of temperature, and wind flow is generally geostrophic—along the isobars—so that the temperature patterns by themselves suffice to give quite a comprehensive picture of the climatology of that section of the atmosphere.

Three weekly patterns may be detailed to illustrate the nature and extent of the seasonal changes.

(i) FROM JUNE 19TH—25TH, 1963 (Fig. 14a)
The temperature map shows a simple pattern in which the isotherms roughly follow the parallels (lines of latitude). The overall tempera-

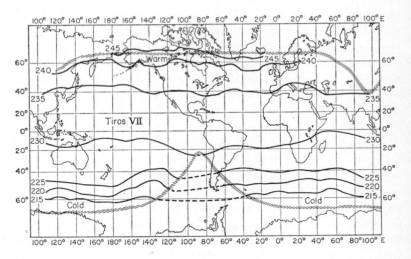

14a

ture gradient is from the high temperatures of northern sub-Arctic latitudes to the low temperatures around the Antarctic, the difference between the two being of the order of 35° on the Kelvin or Absolute scale. This conforms nicely with the existing physical theory of the lower stratosphere, which claims a well-established anticyclonic circulation around the summer hemisphere pole, and an equally strong cyclonic circulation around the winter pole. Higher temperatures cause an upwards expansion of air away from the earth, and are reflected in a higher pressure, resulting from the increased weight of overlying air, at a chosen altitude.

The simple latitudinal or 'zonal' pattern of temperature in June can be only partly related to the inclination of the northern hemisphere towards the sun, and the effect that this has upon the angle of the rays received therefrom: this alone would lead to a maximum of temperature along the northern tropic. The factor that causes the sub-Arctic latitudes to be warmer still is the length of daylight, which is greatest within the Arctic Circle.

The temperature gradient shows a marked flattening in a broad zone about the equator, and in this zone the stratospheric air is presumably more or less stagnant, this marking the transition from the cyclonic circulation of the southern hemisphere to the anticyclonic pattern of the northern.

(ii) JANUARY 15TH—22ND, 1964 (Fig. 14b)
Here the June situation is seen almost exactly in reverse, the highest temperatures occurring in the region of the Antarctic, and the lowest

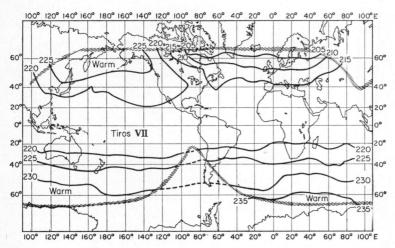

14b

to the north of Iceland. It will be noted, however, that the pattern in the northern hemisphere is by no means as simple as that further south. Over much of eastern Asia and the northern Pacific temperatures seem to have been curiously high, finding their culmination in a pool of anomalous warmth, the so-called 'Aleutian anticyclone'.

53

This apparently recurs year by year, and constitutes a regular feature of the stratospheric circulation in winter, but its physical explanation has yet to be satisfactorily resolved. In the period investigated by TIROS VII, the anticyclone was recognisable in the first week of December, and it remained in position throughout the winter. Perhaps this is one area of the stratosphere that is affected markedly by the troposphere and the surface of the earth beneath.

(iii) SEPTEMBER 25TH—OCTOBER 1ST, 1963 (Fig. 14c)
This was a period of transition between the two 'high season' situations that have been discussed already. Between one solstice and another the intervening months must involve a steady change from

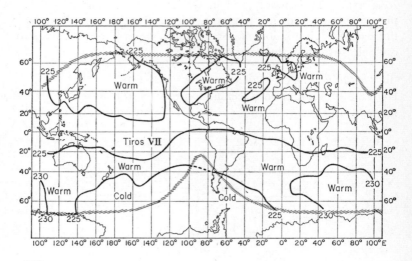

14c

one pattern to the other, with the result that during the greater part of the year the stratosphere contains a rather complex distribution of high and low pressure centres, although the overall range of temperature, from the warmest to the coolest air, may be as little as 10° K. The pattern in late March and early April might be expected to conform quite closely to that depicted in Figure 14c.

There can be little doubt that these maps grossly over-simplify the actual temperature variations within the stratosphere, but they are important in that they demonstrate the potential of the weather satellite to examine the upper atmosphere on a global scale more uniformly and more regularly than balloons or rockets have done in the past.

## The general circulation of the troposphere

Turning next to the troposphere, much more complicated problems are involved. The troposphere is the most important layer of the atmosphere in that the whole human race lives within it; it contains about three-quarters of the atmosphere by weight; it includes almost all the water vapour in the atmosphere; and, being bounded by the effective upper limit of convection from the surface of the earth, it is the layer affected by the pollution that results from man's combustion of fossil fuels. The separateness of the troposphere is never more dramatically apparent than when, flying at altitudes approaching those of the tropopause, this upper boundary can be frequently discerned as a smudgy grey line, above which is the one true 'clean air zone' of the atmosphere, unpolluted from below. It is within the troposphere that the mobile weather systems affecting man are completely contained; it is here that seasonal patterns of insolation heating are most confused by the distribution of land and sea; it is here that most clouds form and dissipate; it is here, paradoxically, that the weather from day to day and from season to season, varies both infinitely more, and even less, than that in the stratosphere above.

It has long been recognised that although the incoming short-wave radiation from the sun heats the earth and the troposphere more efficiently in tropical than in polar latitudes, over the year as a whole, the outward flow of long-wave radiation from the earth-atmosphere system towards Space varies less from equator to poles. Lower latitudes enjoy a net surplus of energy input from the sun during the year, whereas higher latitudes suffer a net loss. It can be demonstrated, however, that there is a transport of heat energy from the tropics towards the poles by components of the circulatory system, and this prevents the temperature gradients at the earth's surface from becoming more and more marked with the passing of time.

In order to understand the basic components of the general circulation, it is necessary to view the troposphere in a three-dimensional way, as illustrated by Figs. 15a and 15b. In plan, it should be noted that the predominant wind directions are not directly meridional, but flow is from the south-west or north-east in the northern hemisphere, and from the south-east or north-west in the southern hemisphere, the deflections being induced by the Coriolis effects, on a *rotating* globe. The circulatory cells in the tropical regions on either side of the equator involve strong convection currents in the equatorial zone, and the polewards transport of heat energy by the upper air easterlies; subsidence takes place in subtropical latitudes, whence

55

some of the heat energy may be moved further from the equator in the westerly winds, whilst there is a return flow of air towards the equator in the lower tropospheric trades. The westerlies continue the polewards transfer until the cold polar easterlies are confronted along one of the most active meteorological battlelines, the polar front. It is along this frontal zone that most temperate, or extra-tropical, depressions form, and the warmer air is, as it were, ingested and digested as the depressions mature and dissipate, and help to alleviate the low temperatures of the cold polar air.

The strong horizontal temperature gradients that develop along the polar front, where warm and cool air are closely juxtaposed, lead

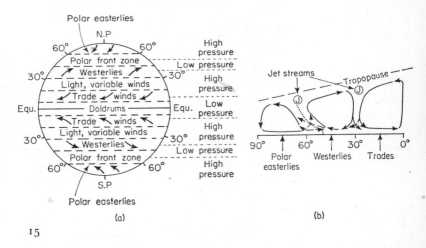

(a)                                        (b)

15

to the generation of the powerful jet streams that flow in the upper troposphere, and sometimes perturb the tropopause along their line of motion.

Thus, although basically the belts of pressure in the lower troposphere are arranged in a latitudinal way, the movements of winds and weather systems from one latitude to another are critical in terms of the transport of heat energy that subdues the temperature in-equalities which inevitably exist between the tropics and the poles. The incoming solar radiation to be expected at any point on earth can be calculated theoretically. The amounts of radiation that are lost by scattering or back-reflection into Space depend upon a variety of factors that may change from one place, and one season, to another. The broad-channel radiometer of the TIROS satellites, measuring the outgoing radiation from the earth in the $7-30\mu$ region, is providing the information that will enable meteorologists to map

56

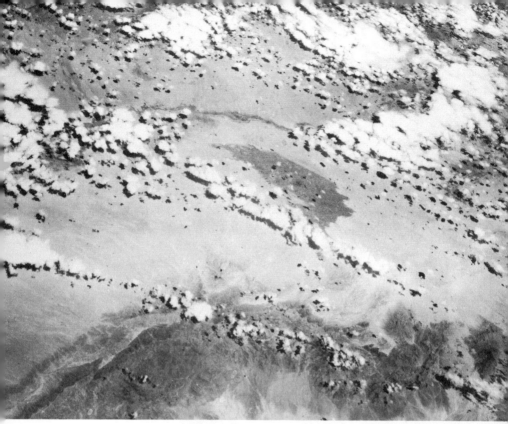

1a

Cumulus cloudiness over the New Mexican Desert, as seen from the VIKING 11 Rocket at an altitude of 55 miles above sea-level on 24 May 1954. The area covered by the photograph measures about 55 miles by 45 miles. (See p. 9)

1b

The coast of Burma to the west, and the Irrawaddy Valley to the east, as seen by L. Gordon Cooper in the Faith-7 spacecraft from an altitude of 115 miles. Cumulus clouds lie along the coast range of hills, cumulonimbus clusters in the valley. (See p. 9)

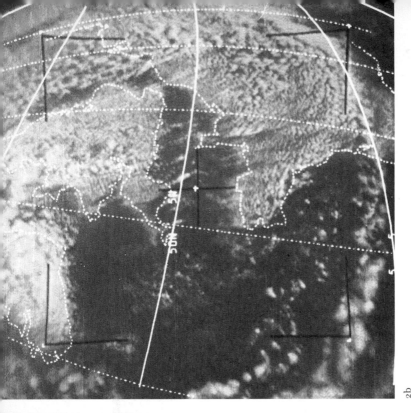

2b
An ESSA I television picture of the British Isles taken on 29 March 1966. Anticyclonic cumulus cells are well formed over the North Sea, and cumulus covers much of the land areas. The definition is clearer than in Plate 2a because of the greater number of lines on the television receiver. The grid and the coastlines have been drawn (rather imperfectly) by a computer. (See pp. 16, 29)

2a
A TIROS IV television picture of the British Isles taken on 14 April 1962. Cumulus clouds have formed over England and France, whilst a frontal system appears on the horizon foreshortened by the obliqueness of the view. (See p. 15)

3a
An A.P.T. picture obtained from NIMBUS I in August 1964 by a station at Lannion, France, showing broken cloudiness over the central Mediterranean. (See pp. 20–2)

3b
A High Resolution Infra-red picture taken during the night in August 1964 over the Western Mediterranean. The latitudinal 'stretching' results from the facsimile technique that was employed to obtain a pictorial image from NIMBUS I H.R.I.R. data. (See pp. 27–8)

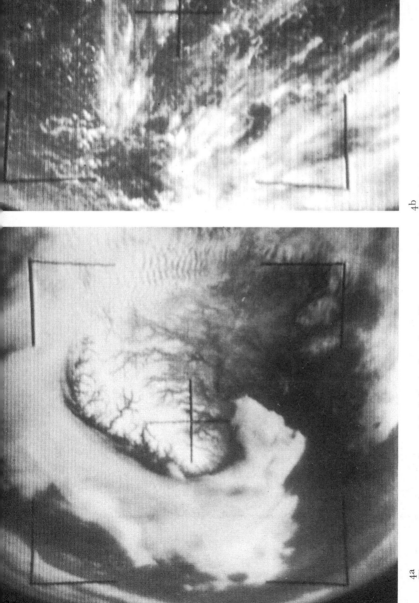

4a
The snow-covered mountains and dark fjords of southern Norway are clearly visible in this TIROS IX photograph, taken on 1 April 1965. Sea-fog and stratus lies offshore, and the immediate vicinity of the coast is cloud-free due to drainage of cold air from the elevated land. Lee wave clouds are visible over central Sweden. (See p. 34)

4b
TIROS VI took this photograph on 28 September 1962. North is towards the top. The cloudiness in the south-western corner was part of hurricane Freda in the western North Pacific; the small vortex further east was not readily apparent from the map analyses of the area. (See pp. 38–9)

5a
Hurricane Amy, as seen by TIROS V on 31 August 1962. The dense low-level cloudiness of the vortex shows clearly through the pale grey cirrus shield, and the hurricane eye is visible in the centre of the storm. (See p. 69)

5b
A mosaic of Project Mercury photographs taken on 13 September 1961, showing a section of hurricane Debbie. (See p. 69)

ER CONVECTIVE BAND

ANNULAR ZONE

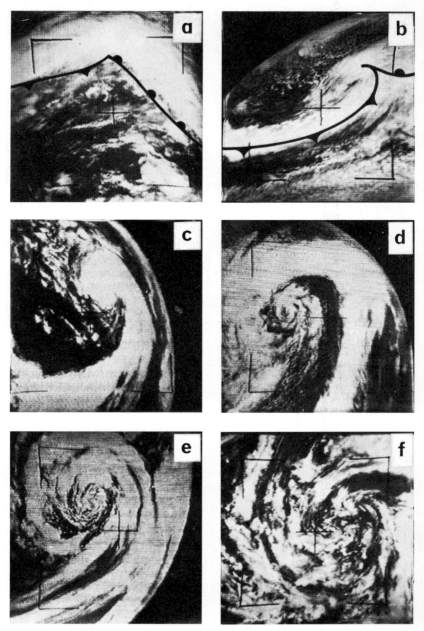

6
Stages in the lives of temperate depressions as seen by TIROS satellites. These are fully discussed in Chapter 6.

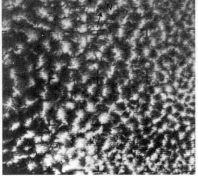

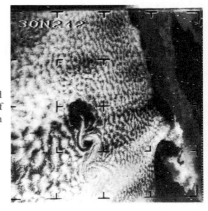

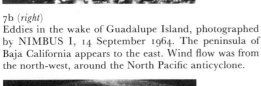

7a (*left*)
Cellular stratocumulus viewed by NIMBUS I, 6 September 1964. 'Closed' cells tend to occur in the south, 'open' cells in the north and east. The area covered is in the central North Pacific, and the average size of the cells about 20 miles across.

7b (*right*)
Eddies in the wake of Guadalupe Island, photographed by NIMBUS I, 14 September 1964. The peninsula of Baja California appears to the east. Wind flow was from the north-west, around the North Pacific anticyclone.

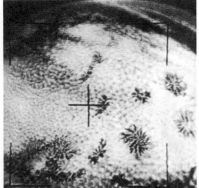

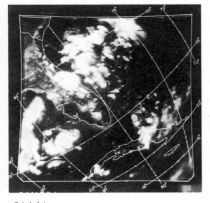

7c
Actinoform cloud patterns viewed by TIROS VIII, 18 July 1964.

7d
North Pacific cloudiness viewed by TIROS VII, 30 September 1964.

7e (*left*)
A gridded TIROS V photograph, 20 August 1962, showing thunder-cloud complexes in the Florida region.

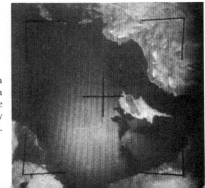

7f (*right*)
A TIROS VIII photograph of the eastern Mediterranean 23 June 1963. An area of sun glint is prominent between Cyprus and the dark triangle of the Nile delta. The irregular dark sea areas south of Cyprus were apparently relatively smooth and reflected less sunlight to the satellite.

ILLUSTRATIONS OF SIGNIFICANT
ATMOSPHERIC DETAIL. (See Chapter 7)

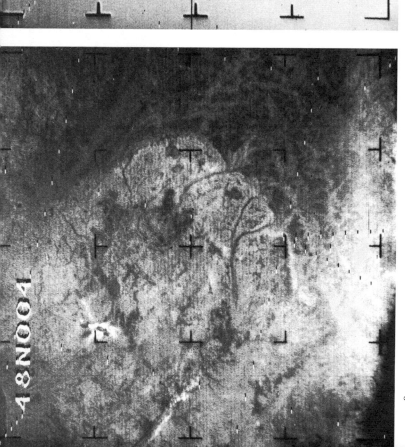

8a
Geological features of the Paris Basin are visible in this NIMBUS I photograph, 13 September 1964. The situation of Paris is in the extreme west, and the area covered is about 175 miles square. The light area to the east of centre represents the exposed chalk of the Dry Champagne; the dark fringe to its east, the lacustrine sands and clays of the Wet Champagne; higher land extends around the east and south. (See p. 106)

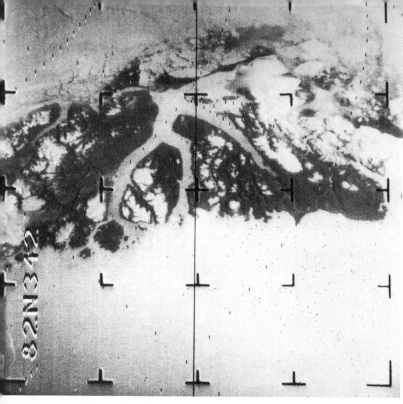

8b
Fjords and glaciers in northern Greenland seen by NIMBUS I, 31 August 1964. The grid co-ordinates of the centre are 81°N, 30°W. The continental ice sheet is to the west, and relatively snow-free coastal mountains in the centre, across which drain Independence, Hagen, and Danmark Fjords to the frozen Arctic Ocean in the east. (See p. 107)

this important aspect of the global heat budget more accurately than before.

Several TIROS satellites have demonstrated the extent and the degree of the subtropical maxima of outgoing long-wave radiation. A zone of reduced radiation around the equator can be assigned to the cloudiness of the convergence zone along which air streams from the two hemispheres flow together and stimulate instability. One may remark here upon the curious fact that the two hemispheres do not balance one another exactly in terms of energy lost and gained. The northern hemisphere is generally somewhat the warmer, latitude for latitude, as far as surface temperatures are concerned, and this inequality was illustrated by the radiation measurements of TIROS VII. It seems that the equatorial zone of lesser radiation into Space lies to the north of the geometrical equator in every month excepting those of December, January and February, whereas the subtropical maximum of radiation loss associated with the southern hemisphere anticyclonic belt is more pronounced than its northern counterpart in all months excepting June, July and August.

Satellites have also demonstrated the expected general decline in long-wave radiation from the tropics towards the Poles. A radiation profile, constructed for a chosen line of longitude from satellite data, is, therefore, shaped like a flattened M.

The problem of large-scale regional variations in the heat budget can be tackled on the evidence supplied by the photographic systems too, by analysing carefully the distributions of cloudiness. One of the ways in which the more important 'sources' and 'sinks' of thermal energy in the troposphere can be recognised is in terms of cloud cover. Clouds represent regions of dominantly upward motion in the lower troposphere, formed as they are by the rising and cooling of air, and the condensation of some of the included water vapour. Areas of clear sky, on the other hand, are indicative of atmospheric subsidence and warming, inhibiting the formation of clouds.

The presence or absence of a cloud cover is always a significant factor helping to determine ground level temperatures below. The reflectivity or albedo of a cloud mass may be as high as 80 per cent, and the daytime temperatures of the underlying surface tend to be several degrees lower than if the skies had been clear. At night, the reverse is generally true, temperatures being sustained better by the presence of a cloud cover, which radiates back to the surface much of the long-wave radiation that would otherwise have been lost to Space. The diurnal temperature range is therefore reduced if cloud persists, a fact which can easily be borne out by the comparison of

57

cloudy weather in the British Isles in either summer or winter, with the clear anticyclonic conditions that may prevail instead.

There can be no doubt that the global pattern of cloudiness influences the pattern of temperature. Indeed, one meteorologist (J. Adem) has developed a thermodynamical model for the prediction of seasonal mean temperatures on the earth's surface, in which model the only independent parameter is the *amount of cloud*. Since weather satellites are well suited for the investigation of the distribution of cloudiness on a global scale, it is not surprising that at least two different methods of analysing satellite photographs for this purpose have already been developed and tried with encouraging results. Both methods afford interesting possibilities for the future, and may be summarised in turn.

### A METHOD USING TIROS PHOTOGRAPHS

1500 TIROS photographs, covering the globe from 60°N to 60°S during a three month period in 1961 were analysed by Arking in a computer-based programme. The television pictures are transmitted from the satellite to the C.D.A. station in a numerical form, the digits relating to the brightness of the photographic image. This information, apart from being reconstructed visually on a television screen, is recorded, in the form in which it is received, on recorder tape. The tapes were sampled at 500 points along each television scan line, so that for each photograph an array of 500 squared numbers was obtained, each number representing a brightness level. The critical problem that had to be solved subjectively was that of distinguishing cloudy from cloud-free areas. For every photograph or pass sequence of photographs a threshold had to be determined individually because of the many variable factors on which brightness depends. Each picture was then divided by the computer into 121 blocks of equal size, and cloudiness assessed for each block taking into account the range and proportion of the brightness digits included therein. For any desired geographic region, over any period of time, the mean cloud cover could then be calculated in a percentage form from all the available blocks analysed by the computer.

Although the majority of the photographs used in this project lay over the northern hemisphere from eastern Asia to central Europe, and parts of northern Asia and the southern Pacific were inadequately represented, the results conformed well with the generalities of the theoretically expected distribution of cloud. The mode of analysis is a promising one, since the lion's share of the work is carried out by computer, and the advent of sun-synchronous satellites viewing the

58

same area of the globe at the same local time day after day will simplify the problem of deciding upon threshold values separating cloudy from non-cloudy areas.

A METHOD BASED ON NEPHANALYSES

In studying a number of different categories of cloudiness it was considered worthwhile by Clapp to work with the cloud charts drawn from the satellite photographs rather than with the photographs themselves. The earlier nephanalyses portrayed seven categories of cloudiness, namely clear skies, clear with scattered clouds, scattered clouds, scattered and broken clouds, broken clouds, broken and overcast cloudiness, and, finally, overcast conditions. These could be related to an average percentage cloud cover in each case. Every available nephanalysis for the period extending from March 1962 until February 1963 was utilised, and cloud percentages for each month were tabulated by reading off the nephanalysis value at every 5° intersection of latitude and longitude across the areas covered by the cloud charts. Although the percentage cloudiness for each nephanalysis category of cloud cover was an approximation, and there was some overlap between adjacent categories, Clapp compiled an interesting set of maps which he then compared with others compiled from conventional data some years before by Landsberg. Once again the general patterns corresponded well, but the satellite-derived maps showed a more complex, more detailed distribution. Although this may be attributed in part to the fact that the satellite maps referred to single seasons, and did not pretend to portray 'normal' cloudiness, there can be no doubt that they represent cloudiness much more accurately especially in the wide areas of sparse conventional data.

Viewing weather on a global scale

It is much easier to obtain a comprehensive picture of the weather systems of the world by satellite than by conventional means. *The Frontispiece* is the first photomosaic that was put together for the world as a whole (excluding only the immediately polar regions), and it portrays many of the large-scale features of the world's weather as seen by TIROS IX on February 13th, 1965.

Lines of cloud indicating the zones of intertropical convergence appear clearly across the Atlantic and Pacific oceans in the vicinity of the equator. Tightly coiled tropical storms can be seen in the regions of the South China Sea, and the Indian Ocean west of Mauritius. The cloud-free areas are associated mainly with the desert belts and the stable subtropical oceanic anticyclones—for example the areas to the east of Florida, west from California, and over western Spain and Portugal. In the middle and high latitudes belts of intermittent cloudiness correspond to depression belts, for example over north-western Europe, the northern Pacific Ocean, and, notably, as a continuous feature around the southern oceans. Although the scale of the photograph as reproduced here is very small, and the mosaic has lost some of its sharpness in the course of several stages of reproduction, some finer details of regional atmospheric variations can still be seen. This kind of display demonstrates the reality of the more important components of the general circulation and can serve as a basis for the recognition and scrutiny of relationships between anomalies in the sizes and positions of weather systems on a daily basis across major areas of the globe.

BIBLIOGRAPHY

A detailed account of stratospheric investigations is by W. Nordberg *et al.*, 'Stratospheric temperature patterns based on radiometric measurements from the TIROS VII satellite', in *Space Research V*: Proceedings of the 5th International Space Science Symposium, Florence, Italy, May 1964, North Holland 1965. Other radiation studies include D.G. James, 'The interpretation of meteorological information from satellites', *Journal of the British Interplanetary Society*, 19, 1964, 410; E.G. Astling and L.H. Horn, 'Some geographical variations of terrestrial radiation measured by TIROS II', *Journal of the Atmospheric Sciences*, 21, 1964, 30; W. Nordberg *et al.*, 'Preliminary results of radiation measurements from the TIROS III meteorological satellite', *Journal of the Atmospheric Sciences*, 19, 1962, 20; and P. Krishna Rao, 'Seasonal variations of outgoing long-wave radiation as observed by TIROS II and TIROS III satellites', *Weather*, 19, 1964, 88. For cloud cover studies, see A. Arking, *Percentage cloud cover from TIROS photographs*, National Aerospace Administration Technical Note, D2303, 1964, 23; and P.F. Clapp, 'Global cloud cover for seasons using TIROS nephanalyses', *Monthly Weather Review*, 92, 1964, 495.

# 5 The Tropical Atmosphere

In the preceding chapter it was noted that considerable meteorological differences exist between tropical, temperate and polar
regions in terms of circulation, temperature and, tacitly, of precipitation. Chapters 5 and 6 consider some of the major contributions that
have been made so far by weather satellites to the study of important components of tropical and temperate meteorology, discussing
them in the context of pre-existing knowledge.

In 1963, Sadler wrote that 'meteorological satellites are ideal platforms for observing the tropical atmosphere. Weather systems within
this homogeneous air mass, covering the spectrum from convergence
lines to hurricanes, are mirrored in the cloud patterns.'
The tropics undoubtedly constitute one of the largest single areas
of sparse conventional data coverage remaining in the world today,
and some of the most interesting satellite-based studies have concerned themselves with the identification and analysis of circulation
patterns and weather cycles there. The two examples selected for
treatment here are the intertropical convergence zones and, in much
more detail, hurricanes.

## The intertropical convergence zone
It was noted earlier that a circulatory cell involving high and low
levels within the troposphere characterises the zone between the
equator and Tropic of Cancer, and another the zone between the
equator and the Tropic of Capricorn. The low level winds from either
hemisphere flow together and meet along the intertropical convergence zone. It used to be thought that a tropical 'front' separated
the two air streams, but fronts conventionally mark the planes between adjacent air masses that differ markedly in their temperature
and humidity characteristics, and the differences between the converging air streams in the equatorial region are generally rather

small. This is not to say, of course, that this plane of contact is not a zone of unsettled weather. Convergence along any zone of strong insolation always results in the accentuation of instability, and the intertropical convergence zone occurs within the belt of the strongest insolation in the world. Over the equatorial oceans the rising currents of air along the plane of contact are very moist, and strongly developed convective cloudiness may be expected as a result. From this cloudiness heavy rain may fall, and tropical depressions may form, even developing into destructive hurricanes if the other prerequisite conditions for their development are extant.

The old view of a simple intertropical convergence zone has been negated by satellite evidence, which has shown it to be a variable, often complex, phenomenon. In 1954, Riehl suggested that the convergence zone is sometimes paralleled on either polewards side by other zones of little cloudiness and infrequent precipitation, and these have shown frequently in satellite photographs. Do these dry zones relate solely to divergent, subsiding flow in the trade winds from either hemisphere before they converge along the cloudy, convective zone, or do they indicate relatively local circulatory cells, so that the strong convective currents must overturn, at least in part, within horizontal distances measured only in tens of miles?

A second interesting fact that has emerged from satellite cloud photography is that the convergence zone is not always marked by a single band of cloud. Sometimes cloudiness may be absent altogether, whereas on other occasions there may be two separate, often roughly parallel, bands of cloud. The details and the implications of these arrangements have yet to be explained satisfactorily—here again is a new opportunity for research. The only general conclusion that can be drawn safely at the present is that, in the words of Fritz, 'the intertropical convergence zone cloudiness is not a simple single cloud band; rather, it is a complex, prominent semi-permanent feature of the tropics'.

## Hurricanes

Apart from comparatively tiny tornadoes, whose very low central pressures and alarmingly high wind speeds help them to blaze trails of destruction that may be only a few hundred yards wide, but even hundreds of miles in length, the most destructive travelling weather systems on earth are the deep depressions found in tropical latitudes variously known as hurricanes, typhoons, or tropical cyclones. For the sake of convenience the term 'hurricane' will be used throughout this account.

Hurricanes, because of their extreme destructive capabilities, have long been studied in great detail. It would be extremely comforting for the populations of the hurricane-frequented seaboards of the tropics to know that, even if the storms could not be artificially dissipated or deflected by man, their movement could be accurately predicted. Despite the time and the energy that have been expended in their study, however, hurricanes are still not so fully understood that they are incapable of springing very nasty surprises. In September 1965, for example, Hurricane Betsy confounded the experts by turning from a seemingly harmless typical track in the western North Atlantic to a destructive path that led across Florida to the delta of the Mississippi, where damage costing insurance companies an estimated $260 million was sustained.

Hurricanes are not only destructive on account of the high winds, rising to 150 m.p.h. or more, that may accompany them, but also the torrential rains that often amount to several inches in a matter of a few hours, and the storm waves whipped up by the winds. The reduction of atmospheric pressure in the centre of a deep hurricane leads to a local rise in sea level concentric with the storm, and coastal areas are prone to flooding if a hurricane passes overhead. In September 1928 more than two thousand people were drowned in Florida as Lake Okeechobee overflowed and flooded the surrounding swampy lowland.

That hurricanes can still confound the experts stood up to legal scrutiny in 1964. The Director of the Provincial Weather Bureau in Formosa was accused of misinforming the public of the course of hurricane Gloria, which, he predicted, would not strike Formosa itself. The next day it struck. 239 lives were lost, a further 89 people were listed as missing, and $17½ million worth of damage was sustained. The forecaster was charged with dereliction of duty—carrying a maximum sentence of ten years in jail. The case for the prosecution claimed that he had been 'negligent', and should be held responsible for the deaths and some of the damage. The case for the defendant was almost pathetically simple: the forecast he had made was the best possible considering the information and facilities at his disposal; to which one could add the limited comprehension that meteorologists still have concerning some aspects of the structure and movement of hurricanes. The trial ended justly in that it was indefinitely adjourned.

Fortunately, hurricanes are amongst the most dramatic and readily recognisable weather systems surveyed by TIROS satellites, clearly visible both in the photographic and the infra-red. The contributions that have been, and are being made to their study by weather satellites are most important ones. Many developing storms have been spotted by satellites several days before they have been picked up by conventional ground stations. The paths of most hurricanes are entirely transoceanic, crossing some of the most sparsely documented regions of the world. TIROS satellites comprise the means whereby even the most remote storm can be tracked day by day. The first four TIROS satellites orbited at angles of only 48° to the equator so that these, and other destructive tropical storms, could be examined in more detail than before, and further satellites of that kind will supplement the coverage of the tropics achieved by those in polar orbits. The intensity of a hurricane can be judged from its visual appearance in plan, and preliminary work is attempting to assess hurricane wind speeds from the shape and size of the storm and the pattern of its cloud system.

Before proceeding to discuss satellite contributions to the study of hurricanes a summary of their nature and behaviour is required as background information. Their salient features may be described under four headings, namely the areas that hurricanes frequent, the pressure patterns most conducive to their birth and development, the attendant upper air conditions, and the forms of the paths along which hurricanes move.

### THE AREAS FREQUENTED BY HURRICANES

It was noted that one of the alternative names describes the hurricane as a 'tropical cyclone'. This is appropriate in that hurricanes only form within the tropics, and soon lose their vigour if their paths lead them far beyond those limits. It has long been recognised that they develop to their maximum intensity over the tropical oceans, in areas where the sea surface temperatures are 27–28°C (about 80–82°F) or higher. Hurricanes do not normally form in the immediate vicinity of the equator and they dissipate rapidly if they move over land.

The fact that they will not normally form along the equator itself, even though the sea surface temperatures are more than adequate there, suggests that warmth alone is not enough: there must be other physical prerequisities for their birth. The usual explanation for their absence along the equatorial zone involves the Coriolis deflection which is required for circular motion. At the equator the horizontal deflection is zero, and the pattern of balanced motion is extremely complicated. It seems that it is not until latitudes 5° north and south of the equator are reached that the deflecting force attains

64

sufficient significance to favour circular or spiraliform motion around or into a low pressure centre. Hurricanes are usually absent between these latitudes.

Table 4 (p. 131) demonstrates that some tropical oceans suffer more from the presence of hurricanes than others. The eastern North Pacific is clearly the area of highest hurricane frequency, with the tropical North Atlantic running a rather poor second. It is noteworthy that comparatively little is known with certainty about the southern hemisphere. The rather low authentic totals in the oceans there may be in part a reflection of the even more scanty data coverage, although hemispherical differences almost certainly exist in terms of hurricane frequency. This may be another reflection of the somewhat lower surface temperatures in the southern hemisphere, resulting in a lesser meridional transfer of heat energy polewards by both tropical and temperate depressions.

PRESSURE PATTERNS CONDUCIVE TO HURRICANE
DEVELOPMENT

The specific areas of hurricane genesis are mostly on the eastern sides of the tropical oceans, in areas dominated for the most part by trade winds. The present consensus of opinion is that most hurricanes develop from pre-existing cyclonic disturbances, even though, at first, these may be small and weak. Some of these are the last remains of old temperate depressions that have travelled equatorwards around the subtropical anticyclones; others are weak disturbances that have arisen over land or in the intertropical convergence zone, and have moved across the oceans within the key latitudinal belt; still others may develop as shallow troughs in the easterly winds that blow quasi-latitudinally on either side of the equatorial doldrum belt, although the importance of these 'easterly waves' in this context is a matter of considerable controversy—here again the evidence of weather satellites may prove to be critical. The basic problem that satellites may help to solve is why so few of the apparently suitable disturbances actually develop into mature hurricanes. Satellite photographs make it possible to trace many hurricanes back to their origins, and it may become possible to recognise the potential developers at a very early stage.

UPPER AIR CONDITIONS

Meteorology is a more difficult and less popular science than many because its subject matter is generally invisible, and it is essential for the complete understanding of many atmospheric phenomena to

65

view these in all three dimensions of space, as well as in the dimension of time. A weather system such as a hurricane possesses an ordered three-dimensional structure which is subject to continuous development and change.

The atmosphere is a three-dimensional continuum, and one weather system is more or less closely related to, and influenced by, all those around it *and above it*. Fig. 15b indicated that the general global pattern of high and low pressure in the lower troposphere is the reverse of that in the upper troposphere. One of the basic 'laws' describing the behaviour of the atmosphere suggests that, moving upwards through the troposphere, two or more successive layers are encountered that are characterised by a reversal of the pressure pattern of the layer below. If, near the ground surface, atmospheric pressure is low, and there is inflow and convergence of air, then there is likely to be relatively high pressure, and an outflow and divergence of air aloft. If pressure at the surface is to fall, as it does in cyclogenesis, then there must be a stronger divergence of air in the middle or upper troposphere than there is convergence below. Otherwise the low level depression must stagnate or 'fill'.

Unless conditions *throughout* the troposphere are conducive to it, hurricane formation is precluded. In the lower troposphere, the air that is drawn into an incipient hurricane is very warm and very moist. As it moves in towards lower pressure, the adiabatic expansion and cooling that might be expected in a depression outside the tropics is retarded or even counterbalanced by the input of both sensible and latent heat from the warmer sea surface, giving the hurricane its characteristic 'warm core'. As the air ascends in the centre of the weak cyclonic system, it expands, cools, and water vapour is condensed, releasing into the atmosphere its latent heat of condensation. If the rising column of air manages to attain great altitudes without being diluted too much by admixture with the surrounding air, the whole column becomes marked by higher temperatures than those around it, accentuating the inherent instability and leading to the formation of tall thundery clouds.

The upward convective movement by itself cannot alter the pattern of pressure at the ground surface. If pressure there is to fall in the centre of the incipient hurricane, the arrival or growth of an anti-cyclonic cell aloft is required to provide the necessary outflow system. It is thought that many seemingly suitable depressions do not mature into hurricanes because of the failure of upper tropospheric conditions to complete the basic requirements of the hurricane circulation, which involves organisation in the plane of the vertical as well as

66

the horizontal. At high levels, anticyclonic cells rarely occur over the equator, and this may be another reason why the equatorial zone is a poor breeding-ground.

Provided that a travelling anticyclone arrives or develops above an incipient low during a critical period of unknown length, the rate of movement into, and through, the depression may be speeded up, and the characteristic 'warm core' enhanced. In the tropics, upper troposphere anticyclones are common, and tend to move westwards around the earth. Many formative hurricanes are moved westwards at first by the prevailing easterly wind flow in the lower troposphere, so that the dynamic link forged between upper and lower level circulations may be maintained and strengthened during movement across the broad tropical oceans.

If the central pressure continues to fall in the hurricane (and a pressure of under 950 mb is common in a mature hurricane), dry air, even of stratospheric origin, may 'collapse' into the centre. The slowly descending air warms at the dry adiabatic lapse rate of about 5·4°F for every 1000 feet of descent, which is steeper than the lapse rate in the moist air through which it sinks. The positive temperature anomaly in the hurricane core is further strengthened thereby—attaining as much as 32°F at 18,000 feet—and causing the stiflingly hot calms that characterise the weather in this, the hurricane 'eye', at the ground.

Thus the mature storm is formed, complete with its relatively cloud-free centre, its broad, thickly clouded vortex with its strong air currents spiralling fiercely inwards, and its heavy convective rain, altogether comprising a most destructive and unpredictable unit.

THE PATHS ALONG WHICH HURRICANES MOVE

The hurricane track, measured from birth, to death by dissipation overland or transfiguration into an extratropical depression, is characteristically parabolic. The storms mature as they travel westwards, perhaps across thousands of miles of uninterrupted ocean, and then curve polewards, often near or along the western continental shores, before returning north- or south-eastwards in the northern and southern hemispheres respectively. This, at least, is the pattern typical of the North Atlantic, and the western sides of the North and South Pacific. The patterns in other areas are complicated by local distributions of land and sea, and ocean currents.

The parabolic pattern, where it occurs, is again thought to reflect harmony between atmospheric motion in the upper and the lower troposphere. Once the tracks have begun to curve polewards, degeneration is hastened by the cooler sea surfaces encountered beyond the tropics. Just occasionally, weakened beyond casual recognition, hurricane remnants may reach the British Isles as fragments of extratropical depressions moving north-eastwards in the usual way.

## Satellite contributions to the study of hurricanes

### THE WORLD DISTRIBUTION OF HURRICANES

One notable fact that has emerged from the new-found ability to inspect the whole tropical world meteorologically is that the frequency of hurricanes is greater than previously thought. Preliminary inventory work on the region between 10° and 20°N, and east of 120°W suggests that this is second only to the western North Pacific in its frequency of severe tropical storms. That region was not represented in Table 4, on account of the lack of weather data and storm track information that is available from conventional sources. Many storms which develop off the west coast of Central America have been tracked for thousands of miles by TIROS satellites, whereas some of these same storms have passed undetected between the few, widely scattered island weather stations. In the summer season the eastern North Pacific seems to be highly prone to hurricane activity, and the indications are that the average frequency is higher than one per week. Work proceeds on the cataloguing of hurricanes elsewhere too, but this is a slow process, since each photographic pass must be studied.

### THE STRUCTURE OF A HURRICANE

Some of the most interesting investigations that have sought to relate conventional observations with those made by satellites have been concerned with the three-dimensional structures of hurricanes. TIROS photographs have been compared with time cross-sections showing pressure, temperature, humidity, wind, weather and cloud conditions, reconstructed from orthodox meteorological records. The time cross-section is a useful device for the examination and display of the vertical structure of the atmosphere over a chosen period of time. It is based on the normal six-hourly observations made by a first-class meteorological station, and if the chief subject is a rapidly moving weather system which passes more or less directly overhead, then its composite picture is a fair approximation to the cross-section that could be built up if instantaneous weather records were available from several stations along the path of motion of the weather system.

Time cross-sections of hurricanes usually indicate the presence of high altitude anticyclones provided that the upper-air data is locally sufficient. The presence of an upper-air outflow system can be detected often in TIROS photographs: a thin, filmy veil of cirriform cloudiness is often found to be associated with a mature hurricane (see Plate 5a), being centred over, and roughly symmetrical about, the dense disc of low level vortex cloudiness. Feathery extensions outwards from the grey transparent veil indicate the direction of upper level wind flow, which is divergent from the centre.

Many photographs have also shown two other cloud patterns frequently associated with hurricanes. At first, their occurrence was noted simply in terms of the weather associated with them, but then it was realised that their presence must be related to the circulation systems of the hurricanes themselves, and more careful attention was paid to them for their own sakes. They include:

1 The extensive areas of low level convective clouds, sometimes associated with tails of high cirrus, that often occur in the wakes of mature hurricanes; and

2 The fringes of convective clouds (the so-called 'outer convective bands') that are often found paralleling parts of the circumferences of hurricanes, from whose vortices they are separated by clear 'annular zones'. (See Plate 5b.)

Time cross-sections have shown the annular zones to be belts of relatively high temperatures and low humidities. Fett suggested that an annular zone contains air that has filtered from aloft around the periphery of the parent storm, lending support to the theoretical argument put forward some years earlier by Riehl, in favour of subsiding currents of air around the outer limits of the hurricane vortex. This, however, does not mean that the hurricane system is a closed circulation. A constant supply of latent heat must be made available if the storm is to survive for its normal length of life of several days, and this can only come from the lifting and cooling of moist surface air. Although some of the anticyclonic air aloft may subside in the immediate vicinity of the hurricane below, much more must still be dispersed in a horizontal plane at the anticyclone altitudes.

The outer convective band probably represents, therefore, the localised contact between a limb of dry subsiding air, and the moist surface air that is being drawn towards the centre of the hurricane system. If this is so, and local instability is caused in this way, then it may well be that the supply of surface air into the vortex may be locally impeded. The band of outer convective cloudiness does not usually extend around the entire circumference of a hurricane, but is most frequently found along the 'leading edge'. This being so,

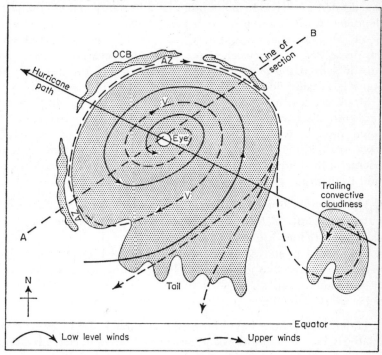

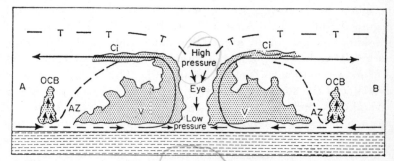

16  T: Tropopause; Ci: Cirrus; V: Vortex; O.C.B: Outer Convective Band: A.Z: Annular Zone

the maximum inflow of moist surface air should be expected in the trailing sector, which tends to be on the equatorwards side, so that the wind flow there is least affected by the Coriolis deflection, and the winds cross the isobars at the highest angles within the hurricane.

70

Upper-air soundings across the outer convective band have demonstrated winds approaching the velocity of jet stream flow, these having been stimulated by the temperature differences near the surface between the surface air itself and the descending upper tropospheric current. These hurricane jets encircle the polewards margins of hurricane vortices, curving anticyclonically round the system, and away over the trailing low level convective clouds. The two are probably related in that, within the tropics especially, divergence in the upper troposphere permits and encourages convergence beneath, resulting in the rapid upward growth of strong convective cloudiness. Fig. 16 illustrates this idealistic hurricane model.

### THE HURRICANE LIFE-CYCLE

Weather satellites enable the day by day development of a hurricane to be followed closely, and their data have been used to outline the

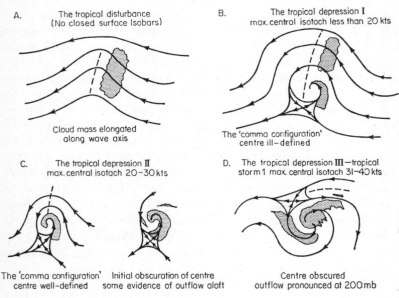

A.  The tropical disturbance
(No closed surface Isobars)

B.  The tropical depression I
max. central isotach less than 20 kts

Cloud mass elongated
along wave axis

The 'comma configuration'
centre ill-defined

C.  The tropical depression II
max. central isotach 20-30 kts

D.  The tropical depression III—tropical
storm 1 max. central isotach 31-40 kts

The 'comma configuration'    Initial obscuration of centre
centre well-defined    some evidence of outflow aloft

Centre obscured
outflow pronounced at 200 mb

17

'normal' sequence of development, as far as one can be said to exist. Fig. 17 summarises the work of Fett, and represents the results of a careful study of many satellite photographs of hurricanes in various stages of growth and decay. The cycle portrayed in Fig. 17 traces growth from an early 'tropical disturbance' in which there is no apparent organisation of cloud, through the first stages of circular motion in a 'tropical depression', to the more vigorous, but still rather amorphous, cloudiness of the 'tropical storm'. Finally there appears the mature hurricane, complete with vortex, eye, and high cirrus cloud veil.

Fett states that an important stage involves the development from the 'comma configuration', where the major cloudiness and highest wind speeds are in the eastern semicircle of the vortex, into the complete, circular wind shield. The stage is then set for the formation of the eye. The towering walls of convective clouds that surround the eye then become the primary active zone, and comprise the all-important link between the high and low level circulations.

What are the practical uses to which this new information can be put? Two may be mentioned here, namely in hurricane control research, and, more modestly, but more immediately feasible, in the determination of hurricane intensity for warning purposes.

## HURRICANE CONTROL

In 1956 the U.S. Weather Bureau established a National Hurricane Research Laboratory, several of whose projects are aimed at the taming of these highly destructive storms. The evidence supplied by weather satellites now forms an important part of the data flow to that laboratory. Since 1962, the vast majority of all the hurricanes throughout the world have been spotted and tracked by satellites, and the recognition of their earliest stages of development is particularly critical. In the past hurricane control has involved, for example, the seeding of the wall clouds around the eye, with the intention of retarding the rate of air movement up through the inner vortex, thereby causing the depressions to fill. The knowledge of the key regions of hurricane genesis is important for an alternative scheme which foresees the spreading of a thin film of oil on the ocean surfaces there to prevent the evaporation of water vapour, and deny the embryonic hurricanes an indispensable supply of energy in the form of latent heat of condensation.

Whether or not hurricane prevention or control will ever be possible depends not only on an understanding of hurricanes themselves. One may be able to predict with reasonable certainty the immediate effects of interference of the kind outlined above, and these may indeed be beneficial. The long-range effects, in both space and time, are more difficult to predict. If, as many meteorologists are now convinced, tropical cyclones play an integral part in the meridional transfer of heat energy from tropical to extratropical latitudes, then what would be the world-wide repercussions of an artificially induced reduction in hurricane frequency?

## THE DETERMINATION OF HURRICANE INTENSITY

The more immediately useful applications of satellite data in the present context are in forecasting, about which nothing need be said here since a later chapter is devoted to the subject, and in assessing the vigour of hurricanes from their size and stages of development.

During the hurricane season of 1962, aircraft recordings were made of wind speeds in the vortices of a number of hurricanes that were tracked by the existing TIROS satellites. No simple relationship emerged when wind speed was plotted against hurricane size, but more encouraging results were obtained when stages of development were taken into consideration as well. Each hurricane was firstly allocated to one of four development categories based on a modified form of the life-cycle described earlier. Additional factors that were used to serve as boundary criteria between the various stages of growth included the presence or absence of an eye, the state of the cirrus outflow aloft, and the degree of spiral cloud organisation in the vortex. Table 5 (pp. 132–3) summarises the criteria that have been used to classify hurricanes in terms of their development. Four groups of hurricanes were obtained in this way for the 1962 season, and by plotting the maximum recorded wind speeds against the sizes of the hurricanes in each group, quite distinct relationships were revealed as shown by Fig. 18. Provided that the diameter of a storm exceeded about 4° of latitude (240 nautical miles) there was practically no overlap in wind speed between storms in different stages of development.

The validity of the graphs obtained thus was checked during the following hurricane season. Wind speeds were estimated from satellite evidence, and the results compared with the actual wind speeds recorded by reconnaissance aircraft. Most of the estimates were within fifteen knots of the actual, and none were more than twenty-five knots astray. These results were quite pleasing, since the winds frequently exceeded the nominal hurricane force of the Beaufort Wind Scale at sixty-four knots.

Given a still better understanding of hurricane structure, and more detailed photographs from refined spacecraft, even better results will, no doubt, be achieved. It should become possible to estimate—and later, perhaps, predict very accurately—the vigour of the circulation in any hurricane. If the control of these dangerous storms cannot be

73

undertaken for a while, then they must be lived with, and to be forewarned of the intensity of an approaching storm even if aircraft observations are not available, is indeed to be forearmed. Probably the greatest unsolved problem in this respect is that of the

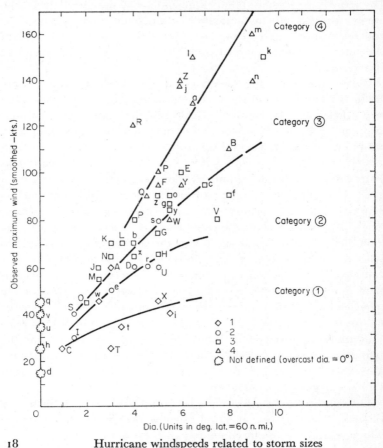

18     Hurricane windspeeds related to storm sizes

regenerated hurricane. Regeneration is a constant, unpredictable threat, especially since subsequent behaviour may not parallel that of 'first cycle' storms, and the intensity probably should not be estimated in the usual way.

To complete the story the final comments that must be made concern hurricane investigation by infra-red means. Already infra-red observations have been used to construct temperature maps of hurricanes and the atmospheric fields in which they are embedded.

74

Maps of terrestrial radiation have been prepared by automatic processes, the more oblique measurements being removed by the computer which can be programmed to reject those obtained from nadir angles below a selected value. One computer programme has averaged data within grid elements measuring 2·5° square at the equator, for all five of the medium-resolution radiation channels employed in a single TIROS satellite. Small intense disturbances of the hurricane variety stand out in stark relief on all the resulting maps: channels 3 and 5 both show a high reflectivity of light from the dense overcast of the vortices, and channels 1, 2 and 4 all indicate low temperatures in the same regions. From these patterns the height of clouds, as well as their lateral extents, can be estimated.

## Hurricanes in a general perspective
## of the tropical atmosphere

The meteorological vividness of the hurricane makes it a useful fulcrum about which to explain broader satellite contributions to the study of the tropical atmosphere.

It has been noted that the distribution of hurricanes across the world largely reflects the zones of tropical easterlies, which blow from east to west between the oceanic anticyclones and the equatorial lows. In the Pacific Ocean, a succession of hurricanes or tropical storms embedded in the easterlies is characteristic of the summer hemisphere especially, each centre of low pressure moving westwards, separated from the next by a distance of the order of 700 miles. A succession of this frequency would seem to require, or establish, a trough line across the North Pacific in the summer season at about 15°N. This being so, then the classical theory describing a simple anticyclonic pattern of flow over the ocean must be replaced by a more complex theory taking into account this new feature whose unexpected degree of permanency has been demonstrated by the weather satellites.

It is in this context that the relationships between high and low level atmospheric patterns within the troposphere become of interest once again. It has been remarked by Sadler that the most fascinating feature of the circulation at high levels in the summer hemisphere is a persistent cold trough line orientated roughly from east to west, and extending over more than 200° of longitude, knowledge of which has been derived from the analysis of conventional upper air data. This trough line extends from the central North Pacific, across Mexico, to the Caribbean, before crossing the North Atlantic in subtropical latitudes, and filling over the Mediterranean

Sea. It is embedded between two ridge lines of higher pressure, in such a way that the composite pattern, as viewed from above the North Pole, is distinctly spiraliform, as shown in Fig. 19.

This pattern does not conform to the classical arrangement either, but detailed daily analyses carried out during August 1959 in support

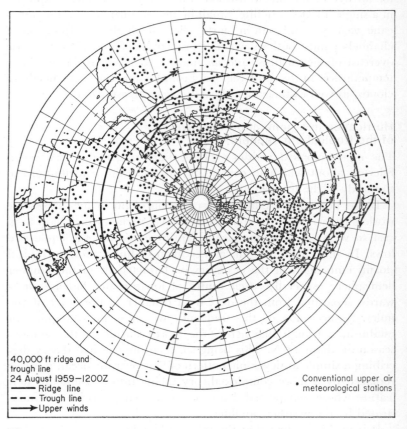

40,000 ft ridge and
trough line
24 August 1959—1200Z
——— Ridge line
— — — Trough line
———▶ Upper winds

• Conventional upper air
meteorological stations

19

of an Atlas missile investigation of cloud patterns in the Atlantic region, from which high altitude cloud photographs were obtained, led to the conclusion that earlier published charts were probably less accurate. The scope of this book does not permit a discussion on the ways in which the spiraliform pattern may develop; suffice it to say that the particular distribution of land and sea in the northern hemisphere is thought to be an important factor in its development.

Of greater interest here is the way in which the upper tropospheric pattern may affect the low level distribution of hurricanes and travelling tropical storms. The significance of the upper ridges is that the general direction of wind flow is westwards to the south of the ridge lines, and eastwards on their northern sides, as shown in Fig. 19. If the earlier suggestions concerning the steering of depressions by the upper air flow were correct, it would appear to be very difficult for mature hurricanes to cross the Pacific from the coasts of Central America to South-east Asia unaffected by the adverse conditions aloft. In the central North Pacific the direct path linking the two areas of maximum hurricane frequency lies obliquely beneath the upper tropospheric ridge line *and* the trough line on its northern side.

A variety of different fates therefore befall the hurricanes spawned off the west coast of Central America. Some quickly recurve under the influence of the upper air westerlies along the northern side of the ridge line, and strike the coasts of southern California or northern Mexico. Others manage to move more directly northwards beneath the ridge, but most fall prey to the dissipative influence of the cooler ocean surfaces before affecting the shipping lanes from the U.S.A. to the Hawaiian Islands. Of the remainder, pre-satellite speculation suggested that only a few managed to survive the long trek across the ocean towards the shores of eastern Asia. Satellite evidence has shown that numerous depressions manage to cross the Pacific, to the south of the upper tropospheric ridge, traversing an area as remote observationally as any on earth. Moving westwards, some manage to retain their hurricane organisation and identity during more than 4000 miles of travel.

This much it has been possible to establish. The next stages in the investigation of the tropical atmosphere will involve similar studies in the other tropical oceans, and the relationships between the trans-oceanic tropical cyclones (depressions, storms and hurricanes) and the hurricanes that mature on the western sides of the oceans. Occasionally a trans-Pacific cyclone might be upgraded to mature hurricane status, but in theory this is not likely, since the already weakened systems tend to be deflected northwards beneath the upper tropospheric trough line on the last stages of their journey, dampening still further their convective strength. Little satellite or conventional data has yet been put forward to resolve these problems.

Other outstanding climatological problems involving hurricanes include the relationships that exist between trends in surface water temperatures and hurricane frequencies over longer periods of time; seasonally, the relative frequencies of hurricanes in different parts of the world; and connections between the number of hurricanes and climatic events outside the tropics. This list can be lengthened almost at will. The concepts outlined in this chapter, as in the two which follow it, are variable both in detail and documentation: research does not often cover evenly the whole spectrum of any one complex problem. The discontinuities and apparent contradictions indicate the frontiers of modern knowledge. At each of these points further work needs to be done.

BIBLIOGRAPHY
A standard text on tropical meteorology is that by H. Riehl, *Tropical Meteorology*, McGraw-Hill, 1954. General articles on satellite contributions in the tropics include J.C. Sadler 'Utilisation of meteorological satellite cloud data in tropical meteorology'. in *Rocket and Satellite Meteorology*, ed. H. Wexler and J.E. Caskey, North-Holland, 1963, 333, and J.C. Sadler, 'The feasibility of global tropical analysis', *American Meteorological Society Bulletin*, **46**, 1965, 118. S. Fritz, 'Pictures from meteorological satellites and their interpretation', *Space Science Reviews*, **3**, 1964, 541, summarises a variety of meteorological studies involving both tropical and temperate areas of the world. A useful treatise on hurricanes is by G.E. Dunn and B.I. Miller, *Atlantic Hurricanes*, Louisiana State University Press, 1964; satellite studies include R.W. Fett, 'TIROS V views final stages in the life of typhoon Sarah, August 1962', *Monthly Weather Review*, **91**, 1963, 376; R.W. Fett, 'Aspects of hurricane structure: new model considerations suggested by TIROS and Project Mercury observations', *Monthly Weather Review*, **92**, 1964, 43; R.W. Fett, 'Upper-level structure of the formative tropical cyclone', *Monthly Weather Review*, **94**, 1966, 9; A. Timchalk, L.F. Hubert, and S. Fritz, *Wind Speeds from TIROS pictures of Storms in the Tropics*, U.S. Department of Commerce manuscript, M.S.L. Report No. 33, Feb. 1965; and W.R. Bandeen *et al.*, 'TIROS III meteorological satellite radiation observations of a tropical hurricane, *Tellus*, **16**, 1964, 481.

# 6 Weather Systems in Temperate Latitudes

Whilst much effort has been expended in the study of tropical latitudes, the weather systems characteristic of middle latitudes have not been entirely overlooked. It is true that these were neglected regions in the early years of satellite meteorology, since the low-angled satellite orbits were not well suited to extratropical photography, but the new polar orbiting spacecraft favour the higher latitudes since there is an increasing overlap of successive photographs from the equator towards the poles.

From its slower start, the study of temperate meteorology has grown ever more important, and is of particular interest to the British. The extratropical cyclone, or temperate depression, is one type of weather system about which a lot remains to be learned. It was remarked in Chapter 1 that the ancient Greeks were aware of the existence of 'vortices', but the modern theories of depression development are much more recent in origin, and even these leave too much to the imagination. In 1887, a very gifted British amateur meteorologist, the Hon. Ralph Abercromby, was the first to represent in diagram form the depression as a system involving closed isobars about a centre of low pressure. In 1921 the new air mass concepts of the famous 'Bergen school of meteorology' were first applied to the problem of depression development, and the diagrams of Bjerknes and Solberg portrayed the sectors of warm and cold air which figure so prominently in current cyclone theory today. Weather satellites have already helped to confirm many of the features that had been deduced from conventional data, and have focused the attention of scientists upon others that have been inadequately treated heretofore, for example, upon post-occlusion events.

## The formation of temperature depressions

An anticlockwise circulation of air in the northern hemisphere, or a clockwise one in the southern, can be attained sometimes without contact between two markedly different air masses. On the leeward side of a major mountain range, for example, cyclonic flow may be initiated because the air gains more cyclonic vorticity during its descent than it lost during its ascent. The vertical shrinking of the ascending layer as it approaches the crest of the range causes the current to be deflected initially equatorwards, the enforced convergence increasing the wind speed, and the deflection associated with the rotation of the earth. The vertical stretching and convergence of air on the leeward side, and a compensation for the loss of cyclonic ground vorticity resulting from the equatorwards motion, necessitate the development of a well marked cyclonic curvature to the lee of the mountain range. Thus, a stationary wave tends to be developed in a current crossing it at right angles, with a cyclonic trough immediately in the lee of the barrier.

A second case may involve an island or a large lake. Since land and water surfaces respond differently to incoming solar radiation, low pressure may develop locally, for example over an island during daytime in summer, or over lakes in winter providing that these surfaces do not freeze. The local relative heating stimulates upwards expansion of air, and its divergence at higher levels may cause a local reduction of pressure at ground level. Cyclonic circulation and inflow towards the heated area is set in motion in the lower layers as a result of the combined effect of the local developing pressure gradient, the increasing deflection to the right, and the effect of friction.

Thirdly, cyclonic flow may develop along coastlines since the land exerts a greater frictional drag upon an airstream than does the open sea. Wind flow is reduced over land, and in an airstream along and astride a coast the anticyclonic tendency imposed by the earth's rotation is lessened on the landward side.

Despite these non-frontal possibilities, however, *frontal* depressions form most frequently of all, and are more complex in structure. Theoretically they may form along any plane of contact between two markedly different air masses, although in fact the preferred zones of cyclogenesis tend to be associated with the coincidence between what may be termed the spontaneous, and the air mass, zones of cyclogenetic activity. Thus the eastern coastal regions of North America constitute a most important preferred zone in winter, when the polar front (separating the colder, drier air over the continent from the milder, moister air over the North Atlantic) roughly coincides with the seaboard, whereas, by themselves, the temperature and humidity differences that exist between the adjacent air masses might not be sufficiently great to stimulate frequent cyclogenesis. Another critical factor there concerns the friction between the air masses along the frontal plane. The airflow on either side normally moves in opposing directions, and helps to stimulate perturbations or 'waves' along the front.

The next requirement in the development of a strong surface depression is for divergence aloft to exceed convergence near the ground. In the upper troposphere in middle latitudes are the so-called Rossby, or Long Waves some three to nine of which may be present around the northern hemisphere at any one time. On the polewards sides of these upper waves, pressure at that level is low, and on the equatorwards side it is high. In the Rossby Wave latitudes, therefore, upper tropospheric conditions tend to alternate between relatively high and low pressure as the troughs associated with equatorward bulges in the waves, and the ridges associated with polewards curvature, pass overhead.

Surface depressions have been observed to form beneath the forward portion of the trough in a Rossby Wave, and to move under the influence of both high and low level winds, whose directions often coincide in the zones of the low level westerlies. On other occasions the growth of a surface depression may be related to the cutting off of a projecting, pocket-like pool of cold air in the upper troposphere after a jet stream has undergone pronounced meandering, forming a cut-off analogous to that of a river meander. The development of a strong depression may be expected especially where a reduction of pressure occurs above one of the waves in the lower level air mass frontal zone. The forward portion of one such wave becomes a warm front ahead of the warm sector of maritime, possibly tropical, air, and the trailing portion becomes the cold front, marking the return to colder air. The circulation pattern that develops within the depression, combined with the tendency for cold sector air to undercut the less dense warm sector air, causes the warm sector to be lifted off the ground, and the warm and cold fronts merge, and the depression becomes 'occluded'.

Such is a modern outline account of the life-cycle of a temperate depression. Only a little thought is required to realise that this, like most earlier accounts, is incomplete. By what means can the warm sector air be intimately mixed with the colder air to give the homogeneous air of the decaying depression? Simply to lift the warm sector off the ground and then dismiss the problem is philosophically most unsatisfactory. And what are the patterns of rainfall and cloudiness that one might expect to find in an occluded depression? The radial weather pattern associated with a young frontal depression is widely known, but this knowledge is rarely a help in regions such as north-western Europe where most depressions are occluding or occluded on arrival. The weather patterns in occluded depressions are seldom described or discussed in detail.

## A satellite view of temperate depressions

Plate 6 illustrates several stages in the life-cycle of a temperate depression. The first stage is a very early one, the depression consisting of an 'open wave' along the air mass boundary. The cloudiness represents the cooling of, and condensation in, the warmer air due to its contact with the colder air mass. Scattered cloudiness in the warmer air, away from the frontal zone, is banded in appearance, probably indicating the direction of wind flow at lower levels.

The second stage illustrates the advance of the cold front, which is now curvilinear instead of straight. Most of the frontal cloudiness is still within the warm sector air, and so is the greater part of the non-frontal cloudiness also. Some small convective cells can be seen near the horizon in the colder air, but atmospheric conditions there are relatively clear compared with the predominantly overcast stratiform and cumuliform clouds in the warmer air in the foreground. This is characteristic at this stage.

The third frame shows an early occlusion stage, wherein a single frontal band represents the merging warm and cold fronts. The warm sector no longer exists at the ground, and the dark area behind the single front is cold sector air in which instability cloudiness results from the equatorwards flow over a surface previously warmed by the prevailing local atmospheric conditions. The depression centre is marked by a disc of dense cloud fringed by dark, cold, cloud-free air, suggesting that warm and cold air are being actively drawn in towards the centre in a spiral fashion.

In the fourth and fifth photographs this process is much more advanced, *and the depression is now at its peak intensity.* The pattern of cloudiness is not radial, but concentric. The warmer air has been coiled into the cold, and the increased contact between the two types now hastens the equalisation of their temperature and humidity characteristics.

The final photograph shows a late stage of dissipation, in which the depression consists of a relatively homogeneous mass of air, rotating gently about an ill-defined centre. The general amounts of cloudiness have become less, since prolonged precipitation and, perhaps, movement over land, have depleted the moisture contents of the system. The clouds are broken and scattered, indicative of the advanced homogenisation of the air.

Whilst a series of photographs such as this can help to demonstrate the salient features of the life-cycle of a temperate depression with a vitality and degree of detail that diagrams compiled on theoretical grounds could never do, they inevitably suggest a number of new problems. The existence, for example, of not one but several front-like bands of cloud along the general frontal occlusion zone in Plate 6e necessitates careful consideration. A broader problem relates to the fact that individual depressions rarely develop exactly in the way that the composite model in Plate 6 did.

Quite often, in the course of photo-analysis prior to nephanalysis compilation, 'front-like' bands have been discovered where conventional synoptic analyses cannot account for them. These cannot be disregarded; their existence implies the presence of organised uplift of air, and significant sequences of weather will probably occur if and when they pass over a forecasting region. The passage of moist air over land may induce changes in the patterns and degrees of cloudiness, and the visual appearance of a typical depression as seen from satellite altitudes may be altered by the development of a 'false front' along an underlying mountain range which may cause condensation in an otherwise fairly dry airstream. Actual fronts may be retarded as they attempt to cross mountain ranges once again distorting the classical patterns of cloudiness. On still other occasions the existence of pre-frontal squall lines has been amply demonstrated by satellite evidence.

### Combined radar and satellite studies

A number of interesting projects have involved both weather radar and weather satellite observations. These have helped to clarify some aspects of the complex relationships existing between patterns of rainfall and cloudiness in temperate depressions. The most useful radar receiver in this context has been the Plan-Position Indicator, which depicts the horizontal distribution of active rainfall across a circular region centred on the radar station. By filming the screen, the rainfall patterns can be matched later with contemporaneous satellite cloud photographs of the same area.

In May 1960, an occluding depression crossed the coast of California from the eastern North Pacific Ocean, and came under scrutiny by TIROS I and a number of land-based and airborne radar stations. In their research report, Nagle and Serebreny state that the storm seemed to be of average size; it was not unusual in its pressure, wind, and frontal patterns. Film records of the precipitation echoes clearly showed different rainfall types related to the old warm front (stratiform-type rainfall), the old cold front (ragged stratiform, and convective rainfall), and the cold sector (less continuous convective rain). The TIROS cloud photographs showed that the actual cloudiness was very much more widespread than the precipitation, strongly emphasising the average relationship that is known to exist between the two: at any one moment of time only a low percentage of cloud over a synoptic-scale region is likely to be precipitating, even within a depression overcast.

Nagle and Serebreny found that, although the stratiform clouds along the frontal zone were yielding most of the rain from the depression there were interesting relationships between scattered cellular cumuli and rain showers in the cold sector air. TIROS I confirmed that non-precipitating clouds were present off shore, and the radar suggested that there was a tendency for a diurnal cycle to develop in shower activity over the land, the showers being rather more prolonged than normal convective outbreaks in continental air streams, but occurring most frequently during the late evening, due to heating from below. From this, and other similar studies, it seems likely that contemporaneous patterns of rainfall and cloudiness will become increasingly important as indicators of air mass stability or instability, temperature, and humidity. The main problem concerns the patterns of rainfall echoes, which tend to be complex and difficult to understand if *instantaneous* patterns are selected for scrutiny. One answer may lie in the use of 'time integrated' patterns instead, portraying total areas of precipitation over a chosen period of time, permitting rainfall belts of a synoptic scale to appear. The first type of pattern would seem best suited for basic research, but the second for forecasting purposes.

## Infra-red studies of the middle latitudes

Infra-red investigations of mid-latitudinal weather systems have been tentative, but encouraging for the future. It has been shown, for example, that medium resolution 'atmospheric window' radiometer measurements may be used instead of photographs to portray cloud distributions, and examine regions of weather development and decay. In the atmospheric window waveband, young, vigorous temperate depressions appear as areas of very low temperature, since the measurements relate to the upper surfaces of the deep masses of fresh frontal cloud. Older depressions may be recognised—logically —by their roughly concentric bands of high and low temperatures, reflecting the cloud patterns that have been described as characteristic of occluding low pressure systems outside the tropics. The highest temperatures often correspond well with conventionally obtained recordings from the earth's surface, which they should do under cloudless skies.

Another type of study that should yield vital information for the flight forecaster or the research worker is the attempt to map the height of cloud tops from 'atmospheric window' radiation data. Assuming that high temperatures indicate clear skies, and low temperature areas the high-reaching cloudiness typical of fronts, hurricane vortices, and monsoonal airstreams, altitudes can be assigned to the temperature patterns if the three-dimensional temperature structure of the atmosphere is generally known. The American National Meteorological Center prepares isotherm maps each day for the 850, 700, 500, and 300 mb pressure surfaces. Using these maps as standards for comparison, any satellite radiation measurement of temperature anywhere in the northern hemisphere can be assigned to an approximate altitude by interpolation.

The unfortunate fact that the network of upper-air recording stations is much less close than that of the satellite measurements sometimes renders detailed comparisons spurious, and although results have often been encouraging, errors sometimes measure thousands of feet! The basic method is sound, but upper-air data is inadequate. The development of a new system for the investigation of pressure and temperature in the middle and upper troposphere is an urgent necessity in this, and in many other, meteorological contexts.

In the meantime, better quality satellite photographs, and an improving expertise in cloud analysis should help to minimise the mistakes by recognising the areas of greatest probable error. More work needs to be done on the efficiency of radiation from different types of clouds. Thick, layered clouds such as strato-cumulus and nimbo-stratus seem to emit energy from relatively shallow layers immediately beneath their upper surfaces, whereas more diffuse clouds such as cirrus and cirro-stratus emit energy from particles throughout their depth. It is not known at present how significant these differences are in their effects upon satellite radiation measurements.

## Conclusion

In the same way in which mobile storms received careful attention long before less mobile anticyclones, during the centuries prior to

85

our own, so the hurricane and the temperate depression have been the first atmospheric systems to be scrutinised through satellite observation media. The following chapter has more to say concerning anticyclonic weather, but only on a sub-system scale. There is an urgent need for a new, large-scale scrutiny of weather patterns in the extensive areas of mid-latitudinal high pressure.

BIBLIOGRAPHY

Many recent textbooks of meteorology outline stages in the life history of a temperate depression. For satellite studies, see S. Fritz, 'The variable appearance of earth from satellites', *Monthly Weather Review*, **91**, 1963, 613, and Revised illustration in 'The variable appearance of the earth from satellites', *Monthly Weather Review* **93**, 1965, 460; S. Fritz, 'Satellite cloud pictures of a cyclone over the Atlantic Ocean', *Quarterly Journal of the Royal Meteorological Society*, **87**, 1961, 314; A. Timchalk and L.F. Hubert, 'Satellite pictures and meteorological analyses of a developing low in the central United States', *Monthly Weather Review*, **89**, 1961, 429; R.E. Nagle and S.M. Serebreny, 'Radar precipitation echo and satellite cloud observations of a maritime cyclone', *Journal of Applied Meteorology*, **1**, 1962, 279; and R.A. Hanel and D.Q. Wark, 'TIROS II radiation experiment and its physical significance', *Journal of the Optical Society of America*, **51**, 1961, 1394.

# 7 Atmospheric Detail

'Detail' is not used here as the micrometeorologist would use it, but in a relative sense to the atmospheric phenomena that have been discussed in the two preceding chapters. The resolution of the photographs from the experimental weather satellites was never more acute than the one-fifth of a mile achieved by the narrow-angled cameras, and the photographs taken by the medium- and wide-angled cameras resolved nominally at one-and-a-half and two miles respectively. The smaller cloud elements and any narrow striations, particularly those which paralleled the television raster lines on the receiving equipment, must have passed unobserved.

The atmospheric details that have been noted can be divided into two groups: those that arise by spontaneous processes in the atmosphere itself, and those that develop in close relation to variable features of the underlying surface. Many different mechanisms help to develop different patterns and arrays of cloud; some are quite fully understood, but others can only be surmised. The importance of detailed cloud studies lies not only in the understanding of the micro-variations themselves, but also in the possible application of the results at a much larger scale.

## Cloudiness influenced little by surface variability

Some of the finest cloud details visible on average TIROS photographs are the rows or 'streets' of cumuli that the ground observer may notice under favourable conditions. They are sometimes visible on satellite photographs as the smallest and faintest cloud lines, care being taken not to confuse them with narrow cloud *bands* composed of cumulus streets not resolved by the television system.

In the early post-war years, when the study of tropical convection was much intensified, meteorologists began to recognise the true importance of the earlier theoretical work that had been carried out by Bénard, Avsec, Rayleigh and others. This had dealt with convective regimes in simple fluid geometry, with the application of heat from below. It had been found that despite the thermal instability that was initiated thus, the first stage was the development of a purely conductive regime with the transfer of heat upwards by molecular means. Later, regular convective circulatory patterns set in, forming a pattern of hexagonal cells when viewed in plan.

Many satellite photographs, of which Plate 7a is one example, have revealed extensive areas of regularly cellular cumulus or stratocumulus clouds especially in ocean anticyclonic areas. These honeycombs of clouds have often resembled strongly some of the so-called Bénard-cells produced by laboratory experimentation, although the diameters of the cells seem to be disproportionately large. A very interesting satellite discovery, moreover, has been the occurrence, in close juxtaposition, of areas of two distinct varieties of cellular cumuliform cloudiness. These are the 'open' and 'closed' varieties mentioned earlier in passing. The open cells consist of a doughnut-shaped ring of cloud about an open, cloud-free centre, and the closed cells of solid polygonal cloud discs encircled by clear sky. It is thought that the open pattern indicates more stable conditions in the lower troposphere than the closed pattern, but there is the need for satellite evidence to be more carefully matched with surface data before this relationship can be accepted as a fact. The major difficulty is, once again, the sparseness of the conventional data from the ocean areas where these cellular patterns are disposed to form. Land surfaces are generally too variable in their heating characteristics to permit the widespread formation of regular hexagonal patterns. From both experimental and observational evidence it may be expected that cellular patterns will only form when horizontal movements in the atmosphere are at a minimum, which will confine them in practice to large anticyclones, and, perhaps, to cols. Vertical wind shear should also be small, so that the upper and lower pressure patterns must both be favourable.

Convective cells obtained by Chandra in smoke layer experiments broke down into rolls or rows following the application of 'wind'. Where the wind velocity is too high to allow regular cellular patterns to form, rows or streets of clouds may be expected instead. The interesting question which has yet to be answered conclusively is 'What relation do these highly organised patterns bear to atmospheric motion?'

The analysis of satellite photographs by Hubert led him to two tentative conclusions:

1. The comparison of cloud patterns and vertical cross-sections of wind speed through the atmosphere suggests that the long recognised parallelism between street cumuli and the motion vector in trade wind areas is a chance one, and that the important mechanistic relationship is between the cloud lines and the so-called shear vector, which represents the direction and magnitude of the maximum change in air flow with height.

2. At high altitudes in the tropics, in tropical disturbances, and in high latitudes, cumulus cloud lines rarely parallel the streamlines of atmospheric flow, and usually lie obliquely across them. The cloud alignment lies along the shear vectors as in the trade wind areas but the shear vectors no longer parallel the low level wind flow.

The cloud alignment may therefore be as closely related to upper level pressure distributions as to those near the surface. It is possible that similar factors may operate on a larger scale as well, providing an explanation for the 'streakiness' that can often be seen in major cloud decks. More attention is now being focused upon the details of anticyclonic systems as a result of these and other satellite investigations.

The influences of the changes in wind force and direction in the vertical plane have also been considered by Erickson, with reference to cumulo-nimbus and thunderstorm clouds. In studies again involving both satellite and conventional data, he found that the orientation of the anvils and cirrus plumes of well developed thunderstorm clouds may be used to indicate the direction of the vertical shear between lower and upper tropospheric winds, as long as the movements of the storms are not influenced by local topography. Where the storms tend to be stationary because of local topographic effects such as those of mountain ranges or heated islands, the anvil axes more nearly lie along the line of the upper level winds, a fact which may be useful in data-sparse regions where upper-tropospheric flow might not be documented from sources other than the satellite. Where the tall cumuli have not yet produced anvils, the vertical wind shear cannot be inferred, but the disposition of these clouds relative to coastlines may indicate the direction of the lower level wind flow.

## Cloud patterns closely related to the underlying surfaces

'Topography' is an omnibus term covering the total complex of surface land features on the planet earth. Daily weather in any land locality results from the interaction of both large-scale and local factors. Different physical situations may therefore stimulate different

89

local weather within a single air mass or general climatic region. Indeed, in a climatic sense, the configuration of plains and mountains, valleys and lakes, is very significant through an hierarchy of scales from the continental to the micro-morphological. It is interesting to conjecture how different the climatic pattern of, say, the North American continent would be if the major mountain chains were along the northern and southern margins instead of the eastern and the western; and how the climatic pattern of the entire northern hemisphere might be altered consequently.

On a somewhat smaller scale, the annual rainfall map of the British Isles owes more to the distribution of highland and lowland than to the anticipated rainfall gradient from west to east expected on purely atmospheric grounds. Narrowing down the study still further, topographic effects of a spontaneous nature result from variations in altitude, aspect, and even geology and soils. Others may be induced by man. Man has long been interested in the modification of his local environment to make his life easier and more comfortable, and he has learnt to modify micro-climates by means of shelter belts of trees around otherwise exposed farmsteads, to cite but one example. Other aspects of his economy have caused climatic variations whose sharpness he has only begun to appreciate quite recently. Thus the growth of cities and conurbations results in the development of characteristically 'city climates' with lower sunshine, higher mean temperatures, increased cloudiness and fog, and more rain than in the rural environs.

Although palls of smoke over some of the larger conurbations of the United States have been visible in photographs brought back from Space by the American astronauts, the weather satellites have only been able to investigate the large- and medium-scale effects of topography on the clouds thus far. In the previous chapter a mention was made of the retarding effects of mountain ranges upon fronts. Other examples can be mentioned now to illustrate cloud patterns uniquely associated with relief.

From the ground, the most obvious and spectacular of these are seen in mountainous regions, especially where a fairly dry air mass is forced to rise over higher land, so that the dew-point temperature is reached around the summit altitude, and the subsiding air to the leeward is soon warmed above it again. Conover has classified the medium-scale cloud patterns that may be found in association with a variety of physical barriers and Fig. 20 illustrates his scheme. It shows that many different cloud types induced by relief can be recognised from satellite photographs, even with the present resolution.

Of particular interest to the weather forecaster are the lee-wave clouds, which appear as fairly regular cloud-stripes, roughly parallel to one another and to the crest line of the mountain range in whose lee they form. The cool, moist air at or about the altitude of the crest oscillates vertically on the downwind side, the condensation of water vapour forming clouds along the ridge of each oscillation,

| Classification | | Level | Schematic | |
|---|---|---|---|---|
| | | | Plan view | Side view |
| Wavelike pattern | Lee waves | Low | | |
| | Crest (part thermal) | Low | | |
| Isolated lenticular | | Middle and high | | |
| Fibrous plumes | | Middle and high | | |
| Large single line | Arcs | Low | | |
| | Straight (mostly thermal) | Low | | |

20

evaporation along the intervening troughs giving clear skies there. Banded patterns of clouds and clear skies may extend in a regular way for even hundreds of miles from the mountain ranges which stimulate them, so that their appearance on satellite photographs is frequently both clear and distinctive. It has been shown that the spacing of the lee waves depends upon the mean wind speed at the cloud altitude, and upon the vertical profiles of temperature and wind. The longest wavelengths seem to be associated with strong winds and a rapid decline of temperature with height. Certainly information may be derived from the satellite photographs that could not be obtained by observation from the ground, whence cloud patterns are most difficult to assess.

Altogether different patterns of clouds result from the interruption of a simple air flow by isolated upstanding physical features. In ocean areas particularly complex patterns of cloudiness may form where islands or groups of islands cause perturbations in anticyclonic air mass movement. The atmosphere behaves very much like a fluid in its flow patterns, and much theoretical work in meteorology has been based on fluid models. It has long been recognised that flow across rough surfaces may initiate disturbances that persist for long distances on the downwind side. Across observationally remote oceans weather satellites clearly have a contribution to make to the understanding of medium-scale atmospheric eddies. Pre-satellite theories could not explain the long persistence of numerous eddies viewed by the early satellites. Longevity is a feature of eddies in the trade wind areas of the eastern North Pacific, and eastern North Atlantic oceans, notably over Guadalupe Island west of California (see Plate 7b), and over the Canaries.

The eddy patterns are sometimes regular, comprised of lines of gently curving clouds. For their formation, it has been suggested that extreme atmospheric stability is a necessary prerequisite. If a strong inversion is present, dry air descending from aloft and being warmed in the process seems to restrict cloud development to below the plane of contact with the surface layer of air. Rossby has indicated that the condition of vertical stability favours lateral oscillation patterns if the lower level air flow is disturbed. He estimated that in a homogeneous fluid only 7 per cent of its energy of motion is expended in horizontal oscillations, whereas in a stratified, two-layered fluid, no less than 89 per cent may be expended thus. The satellite observations seem to lend support to his calculations; there is good evidence to suppose that the eddies are closely related to areas of inversion stability, and that the cloudiness is in the lower stratum of air.

Turning finally from variations in relief to variations in sea surface temperatures, some of the most curious and unexpected cloud patterns that have been viewed by weather satellites may be related to ocean currents. Plates 7c and 7d illustrate two such patterns viewed over the tropical and subtropical portions of the Pacific Ocean. Plate 7c is centred over the South Pacific Ocean, west of Peru, over latitude 15°S, longitude 100°W. The individual spidery ('actinoform') patterns measure between 100–150 miles in diameter, and are embedded in a very broad sheet of strato-cumulus cloud. The bizarre patterns seem to be arranged in rows, and are differentiated from the regional cloudiness by their lower percentage of overcast, and the curvilinear, radial arrangement of their arms of cloud. Similar patterns have been

92

noted quite frequently since 1962, both north and south of the equator, across the tropical Pacific. Unfortunately conventional weather observations in that area are inadequate to suggest the physical processes that may lead to their formation, and they are, of course, much too large to be examined visually from the ocean surface. It would be interesting to plot their distribution in detail and by seasons, to see if they may be related to any average patterns of atmospheric circulation. One common characteristic seems to be their tendency to form in regions of persistent inversions within the trade wind belts.

The most important feature of Plate 7d, is even less a cloud pattern, and even more a cloud-free rift in the dense strato-cumulus overcast. The photograph, taken in late September 1964 covers an area several hundred miles south-west of the Californian coast. The rift is over 300 miles in length, being located near 27°N, and extending from about 125°W–132°W. Little interpretative help was afforded either by the surface synoptic weather maps, which showed the region to be in the south-eastern sector of the large Pacific anticyclone, or by the few ships in the vicinity, which reported the anticipated north or north-west winds and a complete or nearly complete strato-cumulus cloud cover.

Speculative correlations have been made between the different, apparently organised, patterns of anomalously low cloudiness and the cold currents that flow equatorwards from the Californian coasts and northwards along the western side of South America. It has been suggested that in areas of persistent subsidence the cold currents may serve to intensify the inversion conditions. The absence of the patterns in the tropical Atlantic could then be explained in terms of the absence of sufficiently cold currents there. In the Pacific region, the diurnal heating may be considerably retarded along the corridors of the cold ocean currents, causing a delay in the strengthening of the cumuliform overcast, and leaving rifts in the clouds. This explanation seems adequate for the elongated rifts, but it fails to account for the rows of actinoform patterns. Here is another interesting problem remaining to be solved. Unfortunately satellites designed to traverse the same region at the same local time each day will scarcely afford the information required to trace the diurnal cycle of the formation and dissipation of the satellite-discovered oddities if such a cycle exists. The possible relationships between these and other cloud patterns and sea surface temperatures are intriguing geographical problems.

93

BIBLIOGRAPHY
Pioneer work on cloud cells and streets is described by D. Brunt, in *Compendium of Meteorology*, 1951, 1255. Satellite evidence is summarised by L.F. Hubert, 'Middle latitudes of the northern hemisphere, TIROS data as an analysis aid', in H. Wexler and J.E. Caskey ed. *op. cit.* 1963, 312; see also C.O. Erickson, 'Satellite photographs of convective clouds and their relation to the vertical wind shear', *Monthly Weather Review*, **92**, 1964, 283, and A.F. Krueger and S. Fritz, 'Cellular cloud patterns revealed by TIROS I', *Tellus*, **13**, 1961, 1. An important account of the classification of satellite observed orographic clouds is by J.H. Conover, 'The identification and significance of orographically-induced clouds observed by TIROS satellites', *Journal of Applied Meteorology*, **3**, 1964, 226. Lee-wave articles include J.H. Conover, 'Lee wave clouds photographed from an aircraft and a satellite', *Weather*, **19**, 1964, 79; and S. Fritz, 'The significance of mountain lee waves as seen from satellite pictures', *Journal of Applied Meteorology*, **4**, 1965, 31. Articles on eddies include L.F. Hubert and A.F. Krueger, 'Satellite pictures of mesoscale eddies', *Monthly Weather Review*, **90**, 1962, 457; and K.P. Chopra and L.F. Hubert, 'Mesoscale eddies in wake of islands', *Journal of Atmospheric Sciences*, **22**, 1965, 652. For cloud photographs of particular interest, see the 'Picture of the Month' series in the *Monthly Weather Review*. Anticyclonic cloud patterns are illustrated in E. C. Barrett, 'Weather satellite cloud photography of the British region', *Weather*, **22**, 1967, 151.

# 8 Weather Satellites and Forecasting

In the United Kingdom, weather forecasts of two kinds are produced routinely, namely the short-term, or daily forecasts, and the long-term, monthly forecasts. It has been proved that weather satellites can be very useful in the preparation of the former, and in time, should be able to contribute valuable data for use in the preparation of the latter also.

## Short-term forecasting

The aims of the forecaster must be geared to the needs of the consumer. The general public, for example, wants to know what the temperature of the air will be, and how much likelihood there is of rain. Specialised consumers, such as mariners, are more keenly interested in wind speed and direction, and market gardeners in the danger of frost. The usefulness of satellite data must be considered in the context of the methods and problems of forecasting all these variables from conventional data sources.

Weather forecasting cannot yet claim to be an exact science. The chemist or the physicist may be able to predict the results of many of his experiments with confidence, and in great mathematical detail. Predicting changes in the atmosphere, however, is very much more difficult, if not quite impossible. It has been stressed that the atmosphere is a three-dimensional entity, and always acts as such; the precise nature of the relationship between changes in different layers, though, is not always easy to recognise or understand. Moreover, the atmosphere has a definite 'memory' for what has gone before, and no weather system can be traced from a simple starting point in the way that many scientific experiments can. The atmosphere never achieves a steady state—it is always seeking to do so, but the march of the seasons stimulates constant atmospheric change: as the earth changes its attitude to the sun, so the patterns of intercepted radiation from the sun change too, and it is energy from the sun that drives the weather systems of the world. In the summer of 1965, the National Meteorological Center of the U.S.A. paid tacit acknowledgement to the complexity of the forecasting problem by the precedent of beginning to issue their short-term forecasts in 'probability' terms. Their forecasts are no longer phrased in terms of verbal likelihoods, but in the percentage probabilities that certain types of weather will occur. One day forecasting may become exact, but that day is far distant.

There are two basic stages in the preparation of a short-term forecast. The first involves the preparation of the forecast, or prognostic charts, and the second, deciding upon the weather that will probably result. Computers are being used more and more to monitor incoming weather observations, to remove any spurious observations, and to predict the shapes of selected pressure surfaces at the ends of chosen periods of time. In the 'forecasting equation' the unknown quantity is the future height of each pressure surface across a grid network of points. The predicted patterns of the different pressure surfaces may even be drawn by the computer itself in map form. From the resulting charts, whether manually or automatically drawn, temperatures can be predicted for all excepting the lowest levels of the troposphere, since in the middle and upper troposphere isobars and isotherms tend to parallel one another. From the pressure charts the speeds and directions of the upper level winds can be inferred.

It is then left to the human forecaster to decide upon, and sketch in on the charts, the positions of the fronts between adjacent air masses, and to prejudge the weather that might be expected to result from the movement of the various air masses and weather systems. It is in this connection that detailed atmospheric models are most useful, each summarising in an idealised way the rainfall, wind and cloudiness that might be expected to accompany a certain three-dimensional pressure arrangement. The forecaster must learn to recognise the preferred pattern of development of the more frequent weather systems, and to understand the ways in which the peculiar arrangements of land and sea, relief and ocean currents, may be expected to induce deviations therefrom within his own region of responsibility.

Despite all the accumulated 'skill' and experience that is poured into the preparation of every forecast, the fallibility of the forecasting method is all too well known. In November 1965, Dr. B.J. Mason, the new Director-General of the British Meteorological Office issued some interesting statistics at the inauguration of COMET, the new forecasting computer. Mason stated that the evening forecasts as broadcast by the B.B.C. were correct 77 times out of 100, and the morning forecasts 84 times out of 100. With the new computer, it was expected that there would be a steady improvement in forecasting accuracy.

It is doubtful whether it would be easy to convince the average citizen of the United Kingdom that a level of forecasting accuracy as high as that is ever achieved in fact. There are, for example, many occasions on which even the most detailed local forecasts are not detailed enough to account for every local microclimatic situation, in which the weather may seem to differ significantly from that 'promised' by the B.B.C. Weather satellites cannot yet contribute much help to the solution of these local patterns of weather variation, but their usefulness on a large scale cannot be denied.

Another major factor affecting the accuracy of short-term forecasting is the available knowledge of the approaching atmospheric systems. The more rapidly those systems are moving, the more difficult forecasting becomes. Unfortunately the weather they bring is likely to be amongst the most dramatic, and the layman is predisposed to remember the forecasting failures then, rather than consistent successes achieved during periods of quieter weather. The proximity of the Atlantic Ocean has always been a big problem to British forecasters, who have been hampered by the sparseness of weather ships across the regions whence many of the British weather systems come. Weather satellites are helping to improve the data coverage there.

Over the British Isles about fifty stations regularly report a comprehensive selection of weather information to the Central Forecasting Office at three- or six-hourly intervals. This is a coarse network, but the network of stations regularly investigating the upper air conditions is much more so. Despite the fact that the forecaster views the pressure pattern at the 500 mb level (about 18,000 feet above sea-level) as one of the most important from a prognostic point of view, only nine land-based stations, and a few weather ships dispersed over vast areas of neighbouring ocean provide upper level information by means of regular radiosonde balloon flights. Weather satellites will become useful indirectly here if the scheme involving free-flying, constant-level balloons, detailed in the final chapter, becomes an operational reality.

The ability of the photo-interpreter to distinguish middle and upper tropospheric low pressure cells from the more common lower tropospheric depressions will materially help forecasters. Over the Pacific Ocean, the Gulf of Mexico and the Caspian Sea, to mention

97

only three of the more notable examples, upper level cyclonic cloud systems have been seen to develop, and influence weather at the surface of the earth beneath without being reflected in pressure and wind patterns at low altitudes. Quite widespread precipitation, squalls and thunderstorms sometimes result from the downwards development of an initially high level cloudiness. Fortunately, the upper vortices can often be recognised as such on satellite photographs, since most consist of alto- and cirro-clouds that fail to organise into a spiral pattern. When the influences of these systems penetrate deeply enough into the lower troposphere to organise lower level instability cloudiness into spiral patterns of dense cloud bands, recognition is more difficult, but then even limited ground-level observations permit the correct analyses to be made.

### THE USEFULNESS OF NEPHANALYSES IN WEATHER FORECASTING

It has long been recognised that it is not always easy to forecast accurately the movement of weather systems from the Atlantic across the British Isles. The usefulness of nephanalyses in short-term forecasting can be illustrated by reference to an occasion on which otherwise unexpected weather arrived from the North Sea. The first polar-orbiting TIROS satellite was placed into orbit on January 22nd, 1965, and the British Meteorological Office began to receive twice daily nephanalyses from the U.S.A. compiled from photographs from that source. One such nephanalysis was the salvation of an evening forecast on February 8th, 1965.

During February 8th, a cold front moved westwards across the country, its passage being marked by a fall of 2–3°C in the dewpoint temperature. The air mass behind the front was fairly moist and unstable, giving cloudy, showery weather. Radiosonde data from Hemsby in Norfolk confirmed these conditions, and the only ship from the North Sea reported an overcast sky. Everything seemed to point to a continuation of the cloudy, showery type of weather.

Just before the forecast was due to be released, however, the satellite nephanalysis arrived, and showed a broad north-south belt of clear skies over the North Sea. The forecast was revised to read that this drier air would move westwards across Britain during the evening to give clear, frosty conditions that night. One of the duty forecasters later wrote the epitaph—'A correct forecast: but without the TIROS picture it would have been a failure'.

At present, satellite cloud information is generally passed on to the forecasters, both in the U.S.A., and in the United Kingdom, in

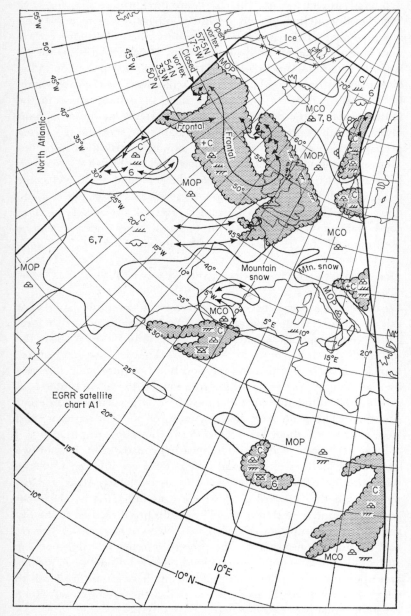

21    ESSA I. Nephanalysis, 24ft. May 1966. For key, see Fig. 12

nephanalysis chart form. The charts are now produced in the U.S. Weather Bureau immediately satellite photographs are received, and are presented to the American forecasters as transparent overlays matching the scale of the synoptic charts. If particularly significant weather situations appear, selected photographs are passed on to the forecasters with the cloud charts. This will always be the case where, for example, an hurricane is concerned. In Britain, prior to the inauguration of the operational satellite system, facsimile nephanalyses were the only satellite data available for short-term forecast preparation, but A.P.T. pictures are now regularly available, and are used alongside conventional charts, and nephanalyses (see Fig. 21) received from the U.S.A. Whereas the nephanalyses (which come to hand four to eight hours after photography has taken place) could only be used in Britain for forecast correction, the A.P.T. pictures can be taken into account in the preparation stages since they can be used minutes after their reception from the satellite.

## THE IMPROVEMENT OF NUMERICAL FORECASTING PROCEDURES

Weather forecasting is becoming increasingly computer-based. For this to be successful, accurate atmospheric data and correct forecasting equations are essential. For some time in the U.S.A. the 'SINAP' (Satellite Input to Numerical Analysis and Procedure) team have been investigating the possibility of improving forecasts by analysing in greater detail information fed to the computer concerning the initial state of the atmosphere in a variety of different situations. The team have taken a series of 500 mb patterns, and have re-analysed them using TIROS satellite photographs.

Their technique of analysis modification consists essentially of two steps. First, features of the wind flow pattern are inferred from the photographic cloud patterns, and the areas of large-scale vertical motion, whether upward or downward, as indicated by the types and arrangements of the clouds. The results are then used to modify the earlier 500 mb analysis, showing the various pressure centres and the advection patterns. The procedure relies heavily upon the correct identification of different cloud types from satellite evidence, and upon the assumptions that must be made relating the clouds to vertical and horizontal movements within the atmosphere. Much research remains to be done here.

Using the reanalyses as bases for 36-hour forecasts, the results are then compared with the original forecasts that were published for each different situation. The levels of accuracy are compared in the light of the development that actually took place over the forecast periods, and the initial indications are that the method is encouraging, if not outstandingly good. In Chapter 3 it was stated that schemes are being devised to reduce each satellite photograph to a numerical form for computer analysis. These are the kinds of schemes that are thought by many to hold most promise for the future, enabling digitised mosaics of photographs to be fed directly into numerical analysis and forecasting programmes.

## THE PROMISE OF INFRA-RED STUDIES

Infra-red data, unused to date in daily weather forecasting, offer exciting possibilities for the future. If it becomes possible to calculate cloud heights, and construct vertical temperature profiles through the atmosphere by infra-red means, then these data will comprise very valuable supplements to those derived from photographs. Similarly, the night-time infra-red patterns obtained from high-resolution infra-red radiometers of the NIMBUS type will help to fill in another of the 'blind spots' that have traditionally hampered the forecaster. James has said that 'research projects have shown how the radiation data may be used to give a fine-scale analysis of meteorological phenomena'. Some of these projects have been outlined in this book, and others are listed in the bibliographies. Suffice it to say in conclusion that a daily analysis of the weather through the infra-red will certainly become a possibility in the not too far distant future.

## SATELLITE CONTRIBUTIONS TO FLIGHT FORECASTING

Apart from their importance in general short-range forecasting, nephanalyses have also been of proven value in the specialised realm of flight forecasting. Satellite information is now regarded by many major airlines as an important constituent of the pool of data from which forecasts prepared for their pilots emerge. Since 1962, satellite data have been used by flight forecasters firstly at the Kennedy International Airport in New York, and then at other major airports in the U.S.A.

The usefulness of the nephanalysis is said to stem partly from the independence of its viewpoint compared with conventional recordings, partly from the uniqueness of the photographic surveillance that satellites undertake, and partly from the completeness of the camera view, which does not relate merely to a network of recording points.

In 1961, a specially designed nephanalysis was issued to a Pan

American Airways pilot to cover a flight from New York to Dakar in West Africa, for experimental evaluation purposes. The pilot's comments were later reported as follows:

'The area on our track from Idlewild to 60° West is shown to have been overcast. Actually it was clear from Idlewild to 65° West, and then broken from 65°W to 60°W. From 60°W to Dakar the map was so accurate as to be almost unbelievable. The map position of the cold front was not only located exactly, but with a 150-mile scan on radar its north-west–south-east positioning was clearly definable. The cloud types and amounts were completely correct.

'Continuing on the flight from Dakar to Nairobi it too was letter perfect, with the exception of our finding some 2/8ths cumulo-nimbi off the coast. This is probably due to the morning buildup, rather than the possibility of the cumulo-nimbi shown at 20°W extending that far northeast. In my estimation we have found the answer, let's send up some more TIROS.'

## Long-range forecasting

For the sake of completeness, the usefulness of satellite data in forecasting for periods of up to a month in length must be mentioned too, though as speculation rather than fact. The British method of long-range forecasting is currently based on 'analogous situations'. In preparing the forecast for the forthcoming month, patterns of land and sea surface temperatures, pressure, and precipitation are prepared for the month that is coming to a close, and maps of their anomalies are prepared from comparison with the long-term means. These maps are matched against those for the same month as far back in time as records permit, and the closest analogues in the past are selected. The ways in which the weather developed then become the bases for the new forecast.

Some additional criteria are also referred to in the normal forecasting procedure, and amongst these is the extent of the sea-ice in the North Atlantic. Weather satellites were conceived originally to aid in weather forecasting by expanding the data coverage in as many spheres and directions as possible. Since the distributions of frozen surfaces, and of cloudiness, can be investigated better by satellites than by conventional means over any chosen periods of time, satellites may enable these to be added to the range of systematically studied analogues. Patterns of temperature, viewed by satellites within the infra-red, will be able to be used likewise. Many other possibilities will result from future technological developments, but their full potential will only be utilised if concomitant advances are made in atmospheric theory, and in forecasting techniques.

BIBLIOGRAPHY

Short-term forecasting procedures (including the applications of satellite nephanalyses) are well summarised by D.M. Houghton, F.H. Bushby and F.H. Ludlam, in 'Synoptic Analysis', the report of a Royal Meteorological Society discussion meeting, published in the *Quarterly Journal of the Royal Meteorological Society*, **91** 1965, 524. See also O.G. Sutton, *The Challenge of the Atmosphere*, chapter 8, Hutchinson 1962, 179. For a discussion of an upper-level vortex see W.E. Shenk, 'Analysis of a Caspian Sea vortex', *Monthly Weather Review*, **93**, 1965, 613; an important SINAP team report is by E.P. McClain *et al.*, 'Experimental use of satellite pictures in numerical prediction', *Monthly Weather Review*, **93**, 1965, 445. Infra-red studies include S. Fritz and J.S. Winston, 'Synoptic use of radiation measurements from satellite TIROS II', *Monthly Weather Review*, **90**, 1962, 1; and L.J. Allison and G. Warnecke, *The Interpretation of TIROS Radiation Data for Practical Use in Synoptic Weather Analysis'*, *National Aeronautic and Space Administration*, Washington D.C., Technical Note D-2851, 1965. The Pan American Airline's Pilot's report is quoted by J.B. Jones and L.M. Mace, in 'TIROS meteorological operations', *Astronautics and Aerospace Engineering*, **1**(3), 1963, 32.

# 9 The Earth's Surface seen from Space

## General remarks

In the same way in which the first rocket photographs obtained from Space demonstrated the potential usefulness of a permanent weather satellite system although the rockets were not intended primarily for meteorological observation, so the weather satellites themselves have shown that equipment designed for the study of the atmosphere is capable of application to, and development for, the study of other distributions. It is undeniably true that colour photography on recoverable aero film, as practised with dramatic effect by the American astronauts, lends itself more readily to geographical analysis, but the black-and-white pictures obtained from TIROS and NIMBUS can make a contribution to the study of non-meteorological problems. Project Mercury photographs have shown clearly, by colour variations, many of the major geological, vegetational and land utilisation patterns on the continental surface of the globe, as well as variations in the depths and densities of ocean waters. Black-and-white weather satellite images have illustrated a variety of surface patterns by means of tonal differences.

Even infra-red investigations have been useful in this broader context. Variations in the nature of the surface of the earth have been demonstrated thereby, including some that could never have been 'seen' in the waveband of visible radiation.

This chapter outlines a variety of additional applications of weather satellite data, and mentions some of the recording systems that will probably be developed for a future family of specifically geographical satellites, designed to investigate the earth rather than its atmosphere.

The key to the interpretation of surface features depicted by a TIROS or NIMBUS photograph seems to lie in the variability of picture brightness and tone. Different physical features tend to be characterised by their own peculiar brightness level. Thus, areas of water normally appear as black or dark grey; land areas in a variety of rather lighter shades of grey; and clouds, ice and snow, in shades of light grey or white. It is not possible to portray or describe an 'average' brightness level for each, on account of the factors affecting picture brightness that were discussed earlier: the tonal differences are essentially relative, but highly important none the less. Texture is a useful criterion in boundary recognition. Coastlines and mountain ranges are often discernible at least as zones of textural variety. Macro-patterns of vegetation and large scale ocean water masses are often recognisable, and the seasonal changes that accompany the deposition and disappearance of a snow cover, and the waxing and waning of both land and sea ice can be traced by studying the changes in brightness and texture over an extended period of time.

That the meteorological satellites have been able to discern major land-forms has been demonstrated by Bird, Morrison and Chown, Canadian geographers who compiled a World Atlas from the photography of the first four TIROS satellites. In this Atlas, every state in the U.S.A. was portrayed by satellite photographs; most of the other land areas of the world between the latitudes of 55° north and south were similarly portrayed. Considerable surface detail could be seen on the better photographs. Obviously many—perhaps most —weather satellite photographs cannot be used to illustrate the earth's surface because of the masking effect of cloud, but all the land surfaces can be seen periodically, the frequency depending upon the cloudiness of the local climate.

In ocean areas, the sun glint that may be an embarrassment to the cloud interpreter, may now become a useful feature. It has been shown that the area of sun glint relates not only to the angle of the sun, but also to the roughness of the water surface from which the rays of light are reflected. (See Plate 7f.) Sun glint tends to be relatively localised and intense when the sea surface is smooth, but more widespread and diffuse when the surface is roughened by wind. Occasionally, therefore, the direct reflection of visible radiation may help to indicate conditions in the lower atmosphere in remote ocean areas, which are perhaps devoid of cloud.

There are also clear opportunities for the investigation, on a global scale, of such things as the relationships between ocean currents, sea surface temperatures, distribution of cloudiness, and the generation of the weather systems that may ultimately affect the continents. The suspended matter which is carried out to sea by great rivers such as the Amazon can be seen on clear weather satellite photographs, the tone lightening with the opacity of the silt-laden waters. The spread of the silt towards the open sea may indicate the direction and force of the major ocean currents; the paths of these currents can sometimes be traced by the associated cloudiness, which may develop preferentially along the currents, or beside them, as a result of the variations in convective activity over water masses of different temperatures.

The general sparseness of ocean weather stations must mean that there is even more that has yet to be learned concerning the relationships between weather and climate and the underlying surfaces in those areas than across the continents. This is a fact that has been reflected in the past in the particularly geographical realm of climatic classification. Most of the 'descriptive' schemes of climatic classification, concerned with the regional variations that occur in the more obvious climatic elements such as temperature and precipitation, have traditionally dealt only with the areas of land. The 'genetic' schemes, such as that outlined recently by Hendl, attempt to distinguish the different regions of cyclonic and anticyclonic activity, to which temperature and rainfall variations may then be related. The genetic schemes usually cover the oceans as well as the land, but the regional boundaries must be less reliable across the oceans because of the sparseness of the recording stations there. When one remembers that no less than seven-tenths of the surface of the earth is covered by water, the magnitude of the gap in our knowledge and understanding of the pattern of world climates becomes very clear.

The variations that have been recognised in the appearances of the continents as a result of satellite studies are interesting also (see Plate 8a), but probably less rewarding in terms of the new facts that they suggest. Although various vegetation zones and large-scale features of relief and geology have been recognised and mapped from satellite photographs, most of these have already received more detailed attention either on the ground or by aircraft reconnaissance photography. Apart from their useful function as landmarks, and their periodical influence upon local weather, their appearance on satellite photographs has tended to be greeted with an acclaim they seldom deserve.

Having made this cautionary statement, a little more can be said in detail concerning the types of land surface variations that the photo-interpreter may discern from time to time. Differences in rock-types and soils can, for example, be recognised in areas of sparse or absent vegetation. Bird and his co-workers have been able to distinguish areas of basic volcanic rock from gravelly, sandy and clayey desert regions, whilst salt-encrusted dry lake beds often act as good landmarks even amongst light-coloured surroundings, since their particularly high reflectivity lends them a whiteness attained usually only by ice and snow or clouds. Similarly, coastal sand dunes can often be detected between a grey land area and a darker ocean surface. Major geological structures are sometimes picked out by clouds, with, for example, the selective development of clouds of the cumuliform variety where the heating characteristics of juxtaposed rock types differ. Table 6 (p. 134) summarises the conclusions of Merifield and Rammelkamp concerning terrestial features that can be distinguished without prior knowledge of the area portrayed.

Despite the importance to the geographer of satellite photographs of ocean areas, and the interest of those portraying continental surfaces, the most significant geographical use to which weather satellites can be put at present concerns the seasonal waxing and waning of the ice- and snow-covered regions of the world.

## Satellite ice and snow studies

The first problem involves the recognition of the frozen surfaces: how can areas of ice or snow be differentiated from areas of cloud if both appear more or less equally bright to the satellite, and both may give low infra-red values in the important 'atmospheric window' radiation waveband?

There are two main ways in which this problem can be overcome, even supposing that there is no ground data available in the region in question. First, the pattern and texture of snow-covered surfaces are often quite different from those of areas of cloud. Many of the more frequent patterns of cloud have been described already, and in most of them there are recognisable geometrical arrangements. The margins of clouds, cloud masses or cloud systems are often noticeably 'fuzzy'. A snow-covered region, on the other hand, especially if it is a hilly or mountainous region, tends to possess a more distinct boundary, frequently fretted by an intricate dendritic pattern of snow-free valleys (see Plate 4a). Second, frozen surfaces are usually less variable over short periods of time than areas of cloud, and once a snow pattern has been identified as such it may be seen to persist for days, weeks, or even months, and may be expected to recur winter by winter. The interpreter working daily with satellite photographs has little difficulty in distinguishing the relatively stable patterns of snow and ice, whose distributions change slowly, from the more mobile patterns of passing clouds that may overlap, or be superimposed, upon them. Once he has acquainted himself with the local situations, he can readily follow changes in the areas covered by snow and ice provided that stagnant, overcast conditions do not settle there for too many days at a time.

Thus areas of snow-cover can be recognised and mapped in dissected upland regions and also in coastal zones, and in some cases details of the physique of the land can be traced where different depths of snow, combined with different types of vegetation, result in slight variations in photographic tone.

The difficulties are, however, increased when broad inland areas with little variation in relief are to be considered. In regions such as the north of Asia, and the Antarctic continent, it is not possible at present to study by photographic means much more than the seasonal fluctuations of the ice margins.

The whole question of seasonal normals and anomalies of snow-covered areas is, of course, a geographical question of great significance which can now be studied for the first time on a truly global scale, now that even the least accessible areas have come into view. Wide-angled cameras can provide the broader pictures for investigation around the hemispheres, whilst medium- or narrow-angled cameras can supply the data required for more detailed studies of selected areas, of particular interest and importance either physically or economically.

FROZEN SEAS

A problem closely related to that of snow cover is that of the formation and dissipation of sea-ice. It has been estimated that 15 million square miles, representing one-tenth of the entire surface of the earth, is either permanently or semi-permanently frozen, much of this being frozen ocean. The heat budget of the earth involves the high albedos of ice and snow, so that the distributions of frozen surfaces are of meteorological significance; they pose very special human and economic problems for the present, and the future too; the frozen lands of the northern hemisphere constitute a little-known no-mans-land between the bastions of capitalism and communism, lending strategic significance to the study of those barren wastes.

In the winter season the whole of the Arctic Ocean becomes ice-bound, linking the tundra lands of Canada, Alaska and Greenland with those of northern Eurasia, moulding them into one vast transpolar area of ice and snow. In the North Atlantic and North Pacific Oceans, however, the margins of sea-ice are affected by the ocean currents which push tongues of warmer water polewards. The North Atlantic Drift keeps open the winter waters as far north as Spitsbergen on the eastern side of the ocean, whilst the Kuro Siwo helps to keep the North Pacific virtually free from pack ice. The exact limits of the pack ice, and the drifting bergs that spread even further from the pole, vary from year to year, and from one climatic period to another. The limits help to influence the positions of the polar frontal zones, significant in the climates of middle latitudes, and it has been suggested that an exceptional development of ice and snow in one region may well cause meteorological repercussions much further afield. In the southern hemisphere, the seasonal addition to the area of Antarctica in the form of winter ice is a staggering 4–5 million square miles, which serves to double the continental area from the point of view of the polar air-mass associated with it. The ability of a satellite to photograph repetitively is extremely important here, since seasonal cycles can now be studied without the necessity of piecing together odd fragments of inhomogeneous information from a wide variety of different sources. Plate 8b exemplifies satellite photography within the Arctic Circle.

The first satellite picture of sea-ice was obtained within hours of the launching of TIROS I in April 1960, and since then specific ice studies have involved most of the weather satellites despite the low angles at which the orbits of the first four TIROS satellites crossed the equator. TIROS II supplied narrow-angled camera pictures of the ice-floe situation in the Gulf of St. Lawrence in the winter of 1960–61, and proved the economic value of a system which could photograph effortlessly areas requiring many aircraft and very many flying hours to be reconnoitred in a conventional way. TIROS IV was employed in a carefully planned reconnaissance programme involving the comparison of satellite and aircraft photographs for evaluation purposes. Prior to the use of satellites for this purpose, almost all the ice observations in North America were made by aircraft and ice-breakers, involving the expenditure of more than $10 million each year by the joint governments of Canada and the U.S.A. The TIROS IV reconnaissance programme (nicknamed 'TIREC') studied the region around the Gulf of St. Lawrence, and the results suggested that the larger-scale satellite photographs could be used to economise the work done by aircraft. Although it was not always easy to locate precisely surface features shown on the satellite photographs, even on those taken by the narrow-angled cameras, the broad features of the ice were often apparent, such as its extent, its concentration, the presence of 'leads' and 'openings' of potential value to the ice-breakers, and the type of the ice, whether field, pack or floe ice. As with snow studies there is the danger that sea-ice and cloud may sometimes be mistaken for each other, but sea-ice can usually be recognised by the abrupt way in which it terminates against coastlines, and because of its immobility compared with low stratus or fog, with which it is most likely to be confused. Confusion most often occurs when sea-ice trails off seawards in a wispy pattern, not unlike that of certain types of cloud, but once again mobility is the key to correct interpretation.

In 1963 a follow-up programme was carried out using data from TIROS V and VI, in an attempt to develop a procedure that could be used on an operational basis with later polar-orbiting satellites. U.S. Navy ice observers analysed satellite photographs of ice in Hudson Bay, the Gulf of St. Lawrence, and along the coasts of Greenland and Labrador, and transmitted summary charts by the normal facsimile network to the permanent Canadian Ice Forecasting Central Office in Halifax, Nova Scotia. Sea-ice drifting westwards from Cape Whittle in Labrador, spotted by satellite on April 28th, 1963, and shown on the contemporaneous survey charts, became the first ice reconnaissance data from a satellite source to be used in an official advisory publication to shipping in that area. In 1964, the Canadians used NIMBUS I for the evaluation of A.P.T. pictures in their Arctic ice forecast system, and for the development of a permanent procedure using the operational ESSA satellite data. It is quite certain that a useful new tool has become available for ice reconnaissance, and that substantial portions of the pre-existing procedure will eventually be declared redundant as a result. It is even possible that the use of satellites for ice reconnaissance may lead to the establishment of a broader international network for the reporting and forecasting of sea-ice conditions in the northern hemisphere.

SEASONAL CHANGES IN SNOW COVER

In order to illustrate in more detail the complexity of topographical information that can be derived from satellite photographs, it is worthwhile to note the seasonal changes recognised by Conover who studied a year's photo-coverage of the north-eastern corner of the U.S.A.

In this region are the Adirondack Mountains, comprising a National Park in which coniferous forest is the predominant type of vegetation, and the Green Mountains, largely given over to arable farming. These differences in land utilisation were visible on the television photographs obtained from various TIROS satellites, the forest being dark in tone, and the farmland much lighter. Areas of deciduous woodland were intermediate in tone.

Conover noted obvious variations in the states of these different surfaces from one season to the next. His findings may be summarised as follows:

*Summer.* The valleys surrounding the Adirondacks were distinctly lighter in tone than the mountains themselves, and the Green Mountains were similar in appearance to the Adirondacks.

*Autumn.* In this season the contrast between mountains and valleys was at a minimum, although still discernible on the best photographs. Conover explains the minimum of contrast in terms of the responsiveness of the satellite camera to different colours. The deciduous trees in the Adirondacks change in the autumn from their summer greens to shades of brown, yellow and red, and the farmland from green to the brown of ploughed land. It seems that the satellite cameras are most responsive to orange and yellow, so that the tone of the forest in autumn on a black and white photograph becomes lighter than before, and that of farmland somewhat darker, thus reducing the contrast between the two.

*Winter.* The appearance of snow varies from the lowland regions into the hills. A snow cover of only about an inch was apparently sufficient to whiten the Champlain and St. Lawrence valleys, and a depth of four inches was sufficient to give a reflectance comparable with that of white clouds. At the same time, however, depths of snow known from ground observations to be several feet thick scarcely affected the reflectance of the Adirondacks, whose forest cover still appeared quite dark.

*Spring.* The snow cover remained on the hills longer than in the valleys, so that the darker areas included, on the one hand the Adirondacks, and on the other the low-lying river valleys which had become snow-free. This, however, was only the case during dry periods; freshly fallen wet snow occasionally covered the trees and increased for a short while the reflectivity of the mountain forest region. At the same time, the precipitation had fallen as rain in the valleys, temporarily lending them the darkest tone of all. At this season, the greatest care had to be exerted in the interpretation of relief and vegetation.

If information of this kind can already be inferred from weather satellite photographs of readily accessible regions so that the techniques of photo-interpretation can be developed to give satisfactory results, then less easily accessible regions will lend themselves to study in a similar way in the future. In the more remote areas of the world relationships between relief, climate, and vegetation, could be elucidated thus, along with more specific problems of economic importance, such as the danger of spring flooding in Piedmont regions by the melt-water from excessive accumulations of mountain snow.

These are some of the suggestions that have been made for the investigation of terrestrial distributions on weather satellite photographs. Relatively static features such as geological outcrops, landforms, vegetation zones, shallow submarine forms, and major categories of land use can be recognised, affording a means whereby existing maps may be checked, but the most useful work has involved, and will involve, the cyclic and the dynamic features of the earth's surface. The use of colour photography would greatly improve the usefulness of the satellites for geographical observation—one could then investigate, for example, the extent and variations of areas of swampland and floods, more detailed patterns of vegetation associations, the distribution of ocean water-masses differing in their temperatures, silt contents, or even in the nature and quantity of their included organic life.

### The investigation of the earth's surface in the infra-red

Whilst NIMBUS I supplied some of the clearest photographs that had by then been taken by the weather satellites, its greatest contribution to earth scientists lay in the quality of the information supplied by its high-resolution infra-red radiometer. Where the sky was cloud-free, these enabled scientists to study land, sea, and ice patterns, in some very remote parts of the world.

For accurate measurements to be made of ocean temperatures it is important that a water surface should fill the whole of the radiometer field of view, since the temperatures over land are unlikely to be the same. One study of temperatures off the western seaboard of the U.S.A. during late August in 1964 yielded satellite values that agreed with those obtained from shipboard by U.S. Coast Guards to within 1°K, indicating that under suitable conditions a high reliance can be placed on the satellite figures. The life of NIMBUS I, although brief, was, nevertheless, long enough to suggest that such questions as the paths of ocean currents and the diurnal variations in temperature differences between land, lake and sea surfaces could be answered by later satellites equipped with similar sensors.

Some of the most interesting high-resolution radiometer readings were obtained from the sub-polar regions of the Antarctic, and Greenland. Across the Antarctic continent, NIMBUS I recorded temperatures that were extremely consistent across the interior ice-cap, at 210–215°K. Around the periphery of the continent the surface temperatures rose to 240°K, and along the margin itself, different temperatures seemed to be associated with different kinds of ice. In the Wedell Sea region, for example, the shelf of sea-ice extending thence to a latitude of 57°S, was about 12°K less cold than the coastal continental ice. The temperature of the open sea around the continent was recorded as 275°K, two degrees above freezing point.

A number of very narrow but quite distinct lines of higher temperatures criss-crossing the shelf of sea-ice were apparently indicators of cracks and fissures in the ice, some of which must have been 200 kilometres in length. Along the continental coastline in the neighbourhood of Queen Maud Land the maximum temperatures in a belt about 100 km wide were 256°K, higher than the usual ice-shelf temperatures, but lower than those of free ocean water. It has been suggested that these intermediate temperatures may indicate a zone of ice-floes: the resolution of the radiometer, at about 5 km, was not good enough to permit water to be distinguished from ice if the floes were fairly small and well distributed. Comparable patterns were observed later during the month of this satellite's active life, and as August passed into September, some local changes in the patterns seemed attributable to the progress of the spring thaw of ice in the southern hemisphere.

In ice studies of this kind, it can be useful to compare the photographic evidence with the infra-red. In mid-September 1964 a number of isolated spots of higher temperature were detected through the infra-red in the vicinity of Mount Erebus, a volcano near the coast of Victoria Land. At first, it was suspected that volcanic activity was the cause, but in later infra-red transects similar spots were seen to form a band along the edge of the land mass until, finally, the last recordings from the failing satellite showed temperatures of 270°K, conspicuously near to those of open water. A television picture taken twelve hours later the following day confirmed the suspicion that this was, after all, a zone of melting ice. Despite the fact that the infra-red resolution was less good than that of the photograph, the patterns depicted were almost identical and the one helped the interpretation of the other. The utilisation of these two methods of investigation side by side must surely become prominent in the future in the tracing of seasonal cycles in circumpolar regions.

Over the Greenland ice-cap, NIMBUS I was able to demonstrate the temperature inversions that are known to exist across the ice-bound areas in high latitudes. In the infra-red, some cloud bands actually appeared darker than the adjacent ice surfaces, and the temperature recordings showed the clouds to be warmer by as much as 20°K: the temperatures at the surface of the ice were lower than those some way above in the atmosphere. The extent, persistence, and intensity of inversions of this kind can be determined much more comprehensively from satellites than from the few existing meteorological stations scattered thinly across the major ice-caps of the world.

If, then, the relatively slow gradations of surface temperatures across the oceans and the frozen wastes can be demonstrated in this way, is it possible to detail other terrain features such as patterns of rock outcrops, soil types, vegetation associations, and land use, whose patterns may be very much more complex? Again some of the NIMBUS I achievements may be mentioned to complete the picture of what has already been accomplished, and to suggest further possibilities for the future.

The recognition of relief is one such possibility. Surface temperatures, and hence terrestrial radiation, vary with altitude and with the heat capacity of the surface deposits, their conductivity, and their moisture content. NIMBUS I infra-red observations over the U.S.A. permitted the recognition of abrupt relief features such as Death Valley and the Grand Canyon. Temperatures along the line of Death Valley were about 15°K higher than those along the highlands rising some 1800 metres above the valley floor on either side. The lapse rate derived from these figures does not differ too greatly from that accepted as the average for the lower layers of the atmosphere in general. Since the infra-red readings were taken at night, Nordberg claims that the heat capacity of the ground in that area must be very large, since the drainage of cooler air into the valley at night might be expected to reduce the altitudinal temperature gradient quite considerably. A large heat capacity appears to provide the only means whereby the surface will be prevented from cooling more rapidly by radiation than the overlying atmosphere.

Nordberg also illustrated the effect of lithology on satellite temperature patterns, with reference to an area in western Argentina near 32°S and 68°W. There, a nearly circular band, about 5 km wide and from 40–50 km in diameter seemed to be distinguished by anomalously high temperatures. In the centre of the band, readings of only 268°K related to a mountain, the Sierra del Pie de Palo, which rises to about 3,000m. The temperature of the warm band itself was 280°K, and that of the surrounding desert, 274°K, all these being night-time temperatures. The evidence of the local topographic map suggested that the warm band and the cooler desert stand at a common altitude as component parts of a single plateau. An inspection in the field revealed a striking contrast between the pre-Cambrian rocks of the Pie de Palo and the superficial deposits of alluvial sand in the encircling desert. The high temperature band ran parallel with the 1000m contour line, which roughly marks the geological boundary. Nordberg remarked that the temperature difference of only 6°K between the mountain summit and the desert plateau at 800m was really remarkably small, and only half that between the summit and the intervening warm band where the lapse rate was near normal. The heat capacity of the desert sand was presumably low compared with that of the solid rock, so that a temperature inversion had formed over the sand surface of the plateau. Geological features can therefore be recognised by the thermal properties of the rocks of which they are composed, and the associated patterns of heat capacity may be of local meteorological and climatological significance.

Finally, a mention may be made of the study of the moisture content of soils. It is a surprising fact that although the linear resolution of the NIMBUS I high resolution radiometer is not usually better than 5 km, rivers less than 1 km wide have often appeared to be prominent in the radiation pictures. This has been explained in terms of the high heat capacity along the river banks. Moisture there is thought to retain solar heat, absorbed during the day, for longer periods at night than the adjacent, and higher, land. This should be most marked in mature or senile valleys where dampness can spread laterally through flats of fine-grained alluvium. In the arid region of northern Argentina two rivers that have frequently altered their courses across the floors of broad valleys during flood periods have left deposits whose moisture retaining and thermal properties enabled the satellite to detect the direction of the meander belt through the desert. In direct contrast to this rather unexpected detail bonus, in humid tropical regions it is not always possible to recognise land areas even of continental proportions through the infra-red, since equatorial forests possess a very large heat capacity due to the heavy vegetation cover and the high humidity, these helping to maintain a much higher temperature over land than is usual at night. The differences between land and sea in those regions is consequently less than usual, and the coasts themselves may be obscure.

NEW LIGHT ON OLD PROBLEMS

## Geographical satellites

In summary, therefore, it can be claimed justly that although weather satellite data has been of primary interest to the atmospheric scientist for whom it was intended, there have been many ways in which the same data have been employed for broader geographical purposes.

Current work in the U.S.A. is concerned with planning and designing a specifically geographical satellite system which will employ special satellites to investigate a wide range of surface phenomena by photographic and radiometric means. Since the atmosphere is transparent to radiation in a number of other electromagnetic wavelengths in addition to those of visible light and the 'atmospheric window', it should be possible to employ sensors to investigate the 'windows' that exist in ultra-violet, micro-wave, and radar wavebands. Not only will surface temperatures be examined, but a wide range of other geographical parameters as well, such as the chemical composition of soils, the roughness, and the moisture content of the ground surface. Table 7 (p. 134) summarises some of the possibilities.

It is the view of an increasing number of geographers on both sides of the Atlantic that the supplementing and reinforcement of data from conventional sources by the infusion of that from Space will free more of their time from cumbersome processes of data collection, for the development and testing of geographical hypotheses. For example, it has already been shown that individual snapshots of the earth's surface such as those taken by Project Mercury astronauts at a scale of about one to one million immediately achieve a degree of generalisation only achieved hitherto by considerable cartographic labour. Furthermore, ground-based surveys invariably involve long periods of time, and the resulting maps may be quite out of date when published, and may even present a misleading picture where such things as land utilisation are concerned. The 'observational platforms in Space' for which Carl-Gustav Rossby pleaded in weather study, can be extremely useful in many branches of earth science by giving complete views of very wide areas almost instantaneously, and permitting frequent reinvestigation. By varying the optics of the Space camera systems quite small objects, such as individual fields, streets and buildings should become visible from permanent satellite altitudes. American army satellite photographs are already being used in the compilation of topographic maps for parts of Borneo.

Geography is surely moving towards a new status as one of the 'Space sciences', said by Jastrow and Cameron to be 'the collection

116

of scientific problems to which Space vehicles can make some specific contributions not achievable by ground-based experiments'. In the near future the attention of many environmental scientists will probably focus on other planets; before moving further into Space, much remains to be learnt about our own planet from that new standpoint.

## BIBLIOGRAPHY

The usefulness of colour photography from manned spacecraft is discussed by K.M. Nagler and S.D. Soules, 'Cloud photography from the Gemini 4 spaceflight', *Bulletin of the American Meteorological Society*, **46**, 1965, 522. General geographical applications of TIROS photography are considered by S. Fritz, 'The variable appearance of the earth from satellites', *Monthly Weather Review*, **91**, 1963, 613; J.B. Bird, A. Morrison and M.C. Chown, *World Atlas of Photography from TIROS satellites I to IV*, National Aeronautics and Space Administration, Washington, 1964, Contractor Report CR–98; E.C. Barrett, 'Satellite meteorology and the geographer', *Geography*, **49**, 1964, 377; and P.M. Merifield and J. Rammelkamp, 'Terrain seen from TIROS', *Photogrammetric Engineering*, **32**, 1966, 44. A genetic classification of climate is that of M. Hendl, *Einführung in die Physikalische Klimatologie: Band II, Systematische Klimatologie*, Berlin, 1963. TIROS-based ice and snow studies are reported in several of the general articles listed at the end of Chapter 2.

The following may be noted in addition: D.Q. Wark and R.W. Popham, 'The development of satellite ice-surveillance techniques', in *Rocket and Satellite Meteorology*, (*op. cit.*) 415; S. Fritz, 'Snow surveys from satellite pictures', *ibid.*, 419. Seasonal changes in the tone of the earth surface are described by J.H. Conover, 'Note on the flora and snow cover distributions affecting the appearance of northeastern United States as photographed by TIROS satellites', *Monthly Weather Review*, **93**, 1965, 644.

NIMBUS-based studies include R.W. Popham and R.E. Samuelson, 'Polar exploration with NIMBUS meteorological satellite', *Arctic*, **18**, 1965, 246. The work by W. Nordberg has been summarised from a currently unpublished manuscript. Several articles have been written on the investigation of the earth surface in wavelengths other than those of visible light, including R.A. Hanel and D.Q. Wark, 'Physical measurements from meteorological satellites', *Astronautics and Aerospace Engineering*, **1**(3), 1963, 85; S.F. Singer and R.W. Popham, 'Non-meteorological observations from weather satellites', *Astronautics and Aerospace Engineering*, **1**(3), 1963, 89; R.H. Alexander, *Geographic Research Potential of Earth Satellites*, Proceedings of the

Third Symposium on Remote Sensing of Environment, University of Michigan, 1964, 453, and R.H. Alexander, 'Geographic data from Space', *Professional Geographer*, **16**, 1964, 1.

A concise summary of the future possible geographical satellite investigations is by P.C. Badgley, 'Planetary exploration from orbital altitudes', *Photogrammetric Engineering*, **32**, 1966, 250. See also *Spacecraft in Geographical Research*, the Report of a Conference on the Use of Orbiting Spacecraft in Geographic Research, Houston, Texas, 1965, Publication 1953, National Academy of Sciences National Research Council, Washington DC, 1966.

# PART III

# Future Developments

# 10 Further Observational Aids

The close relationships that exist between weather forecasting and weather observation were underlined in the opening chapter. The concluding remarks attempt to summarise some of the contributions that have been made by TIROS and NIMBUS satellites in these two important aspects of meteorology, and suggest some that may be made by these and other means in the future.

Before the Space Age in weather study dawned in 1960, there were five major requirements to be met if weather forecasts were to be substantially improved. It would be necessary:

1. to obtain more detailed information concerning atmospheric conditions in sparse data areas such as the tropics, the oceans, and the polar regions;
2. to view in detail large-scale patterns, systems, and arrangements of weather so that the degree of dependence on classical weather models, whose validity in specific situations often leaves much to be desired, might be reduced;
3. to obtain more wind and pressure data from the upper levels in the troposphere;
4. to scrutinise night-time weather in greater detail; and
5. to refine the numerical models that were being used increasingly in weather forecasting.

One of the objects of this book has been to demonstrate the progress that even the 'experimental' weather satellites have enabled to be made in all five of these respects. TIROS and NIMBUS satellites have made a big contribution to the volume of data forthcoming from remote parts of the world, and the NIMBUS high-resolution radiometer has given the scientist his first broad-scale view of night-time weather systems. It has been possible as a result, to clarify some of the classical weather models, and studies of problems such as that of vorticity advection in depressions should result in the refinement of computer forecasting techniques. Finally, however, it must be admitted that upper level wind and pressure patterns can only be inferred indirectly from TIROS and NIMBUS data and upper atmospheric conditions are still rather poorly documented.

It has been stressed that even an operational weather satellite system, such as that of the pairs of ESSA satellites, far from reducing the need for 'conventional' weather observations, will tend to increase it. For example, the observational lead which has been assumed by the satellites over remote areas needs to be followed by a closer network of surface stations to assist in the explanation of many of the curious features that have been newly revealed. Although the existing TIROS and NIMBUS satellites are quite sophisticated in themselves, they are by no means the ultimate. Many suggestions have concerned their further development, and a range of other observational systems are being planned for supplementary roles. Since the plans are subject to rather rapid modification in the early stages, it must be stated that this account describes the situation early in 1966, and stresses the types of observations that will be made, rather than the details of the proposed equipment. There can be little doubt, however, that some of the proposed systems will become reality, and those that do not will probably be replaced by others designed to do similar kinds of work.

### Proposed satellites

First, a brief summary of the probable developments involving future TIROS and NIMBUS-type satellites.

One such development may be the installation of colour cameras. This would certainly excite the interest of the geographer since various surface patterns would appear with greater clarity as a result, and it would also simplify some of the problems of cloud interpretation for the meteorologist and enable him to discern greater cloud detail. Small cumuliform cloud cells and diffuse cirrus cloudiness, to mention only two examples, should be more readily apparent on colour photographs.

It has also been claimed that ultra-sensitive television cameras may be able to undertake night-time cloud photography by using the light from the stars or the moon. In this way, 'photography' by high-resolution infra-red radiometers could be supplemented or even replaced if the scheme were successful. A further possibility involves equipping satellites with radar, so that cloud photographs and radar rainfall patterns could be more satisfactorily integrated with one another than at present, with the radar observations being made from the ground. Radar, using a variety of wavelengths, could investigate a variety of things. Using a very short wavelength, the beams would reflect from cloud tops and permit the accurate calculation of cloud heights; using longer wavelengths to penetrate the clouds themselves and to be reflected by raindrops or ice crystals, the vertical structure of stratiform and shallow cumuliform clouds could be studied, if not those of taller, more complex cumulo-nimbi. A so-called 'bright band echo' is known to be caused by the melting of falling snowflakes, and the height of the 32°F isotherm can be located by this means under suitable conditions. The forecaster may thus be helped to forecast the probability of snowfall. Satellite-borne radio-devices could detect thunderstorm activity by their associated discharge of static electricity.

Finally, the problem of the investigation of wind and pressure patterns up through the troposphere is one which may be solved in part by fitting a new kind of spectrometer into TIROS or NIMBUS type satellites. One instrument has been flown experimentally in a balloon, and has demonstrated the feasibility of building up simplified temperature cross-profiles by indirect means. A similar spectrometer will be flown in a future NIMBUS spacecraft.

Returning to the question of weather photography, a new family of satellites (tentatively named 'AEROS') is being designed to operate at the high altitude of 22,300 miles above the earth's surface. This altitude, comparable to that of the Early Bird communications satellite, represents an 'earth-synchronous' orbit—one in which a satellite remains in a fixed position relative to a predetermined point on the ground. The present ESSA system achieves a complete photographic coverage of the world about once a day. The changeability of weather systems, however, means that a preferable satellite system from the short-term forecasters' point of view would incorporate spacecraft giving information of each area at much shorter intervals to that weather movement and metamorphosis could be followed more closely. The earth-synchronous satellites would have this capability. Although it might seem that their much greater altitude would result in a loss of picture definition, this apparently is not necessarily so. The problem is one of camera optics, and the experts claim that no loss of definition need be entailed. It is planned that two cameras will be used contemporaneously, a broad-angled camera giving a photographic coverage of a wide area centred on the satellite sub-point, leaving to the narrow-angled camera the task of recording more localised conditions within the main field of view. The forecaster would benefit especially when the less predictable, and more dramatic, rapidly changing types of weather prevailed. The accuracy of general forecasts should be improved still further, as well as the more specialised forecasts such as those prepared for mariners and airline pilots.

As a test for the earth-synchronous satellite system, the National Aeronautics and Space Administration plans to launch a modified TIROS-type satellite (designated TIROS K) into a highly elliptical orbit ranging from an apogee near the earth-synchronous altitude to a perigee only 300–400 miles above the earth's surface. TIROS K will be a test-bed for some of the new equipment.

For a complete global coverage by these high-altitude spacecraft, three satellites of this kind would probably suffice. The distribution of ground tracking stations, however, is still very much open to discussion. One station for each satellite would be required if there were to be no gaps in the photography of the earth, but one of the three stations would have to be placed outside the U.S.A. Two stations only, one at Gilmore Creek in Alaska, and one at Suitland, Maryland, would cause a narrow photographic 'blind corridor' to lie across Central Asia, India, and the Southern Indian Ocean. A low-altitude polar-orbiting satellite of the TIROS type could fill such a gap, transmitting its own data to Gilmore Creek.

## Automatic weather recordings

Some of the other revolutionary schemes planned for the future would utilise the AEROS satellites as 'middlemen' for the collection of data from several types of unmanned weather recording stations, both on the earth's surface and in the atmosphere, and data transmission back to selected forecasting centres. The unmanned surface stations could include both land- and sea-based varieties, the weather observations being made by automatic instruments. The land-based stations pose no insuperable problems, since most meteorological data can be obtained automatically today. The ocean stations require more careful thought. They must be able to ride the waves, yet be unaffected structurally by the constant bombardment of wind and waves, and must be fixed in position if their lives are to be of economic length.

For some years a nuclear-powered boat nicknamed 'NOMAD' has been moored in the Gulf of Mexico, transmitting data at regular intervals to a land-based station. The instruments are all automatic, and the boat is unmanned. Such a vessel as this, however, is not

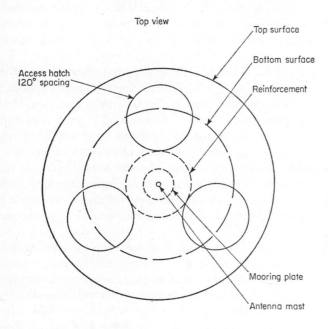

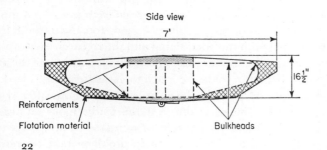

22

deemed suitable for a world-wide network of ocean stations, partly because of its expensiveness and weight of its steel hull, and partly because its conventional shape is not the best to resist the force of the waves, especially when the wind waves are at an angle to the swell.

Plans are being drawn up instead for a new type of weather buoy, (see Fig. 22) shaped like a disc, 7 feet broad, and 16½ inches deep, designed to ride the waves from all directions, and to be less affected by lateral pressure than an orthodox hull. The construction materials can be cheap, and light in weight, including reinforced plastics and glass, fitted together with nylon bolts so that the finished article includes a minimum of metal. The natural lightness of these materials could be supplemented by styrofoam deployed along the edges and across the base, to bring the floatation characteristics to a suitable level.

This kind of buoy would be cheap to manufacture, and the cost of replacement at, say, annual intervals, would not be prohibitively high. The oceans could be subdivided into areas that would become the responsibility of the interested nations. Thus the total cost of a global scheme involving thousands of buoys would be shared, in much the same way in which the present network of weather ships is maintained. Perhaps the biggest problem would be that of anchorage. The answer probably lies in the utilisation of mooring lines of steel and nylon up to 3000 fathoms long, which would enable buoys to be moored on the floors of the oceans in all except the deepest areas.

The buoys would be equipped to measure such things as wind speed and direction, air and sea temperature, and atmospheric pressure. The data would be sent by radio to an interrogatory satellite, and then to the main forecasting centres of the world.

Another imaginative suggestion that is being developed in both France and the U.S.A. concerns free-flying balloons designed to float at chosen pressure levels within the atmosphere. A total of 5000 balloons has been suggested, with 500 each at the 700 mb and 30 mb levels, and 1000 each at the 500, 300, 200 and 100 mb levels. These would tell both the operational and the research meteorologist much concerning conditions through the different layers of the atmosphere. The balloons could be used to indicate wind speed and direction simply by plotting their successive positions after regular intervals of time. Wind flow aloft is more steady than that near the ground, and it should be possible to estimate wind speeds to an accuracy of 1–2 knots. Two of the main problems here concern the possibility of collisions with aircraft, and ingestion by jet engines. The first has been investigated statistically, and less than one collision might be expected over the U.S.A. each year. Even this would be too high a frequency if aircraft damage were to be sustained, so the balloons will have to lack solid attachments, their radio circuits (enabling them to be tracked) being incorporated in the outer frangible skins. The second problem, that of ingestion by jets, is more difficult to

124

resolve, since protective fenders over jet engines tend to reduce their efficiency a little, an unattractive proposition for aircraft operators. A problem of a different nature altogether arises from the free-flight characteristics: free-flying balloons cannot be expected to observe the regional taboos of twentieth-century politics, and it is almost certain that some countries will object to the violation of their air-space by overflight. This, perhaps, is less unreasonable than it seems at first. Although in peacetime the exchange of meteorological data amongst the nations of the world is at least as free as that of any other scientific information, upper air data derived from balloons, gathered up by satellites, and transmitted to receiving stations in the U.S.A. would most certainly be begrudged by military opponents in times of war. Early in 1966 the first few experimental balloons were released in the southern hemisphere (the less sensitive politically of the two) in the hope that these would indicate the general practicability of the total scheme, and throw light on the particular problems of the routes the balloons would take and the areas in which they might tend to congregate—both depending on the patterns of air flow.

## Dirigibles

One last observational system worthy of mention in this present context involves the use of dirigibles, the modern descendants of the great, but often ill-fated, airships of the early decades of this century. The United States Navy are currently evaluating the usefulness of huge dirigibles, 1000 feet in length, and filled with non-inflammable helium. Nuclear propulsion could be employed in future, and this kind of dirigible would enjoy an endurance measured in many months. Experiments off the east coast of the U.S.A. as early as January 1957 involved a constant airship watch on the weather through extremes of snow, high winds and freezing rain, that kept all the weather reconnaissance aircraft firmly grounded. Unlike the weather buoys and balloons the dirigibles would be manned, but the crews could be relieved whilst the vessels were still in the air. Indeed, the permanent presence of scientific observers would introduce flexibility and variety into the kinds of observational tasks that would be carried out from them. These might include rawinsonde and meteorological sounding rocket flights from the dirigibles, recordings from sea level to the flight altitude (possible at about 5000 feet) by means of suspended sensors, and also the collection of samples of air and rain-water for on-board laboratory analysis. Other non-meteorological functions might be carried out as well. It has been suggested by Vaeth that an airship equipped with radar and acting as a navigational beacon would be a boon to aircraft operating over the Arctic; the enormous rigid frame could, perhaps, be coupled and transformed into an immense 'flying antenna' for data transmission to shore-based relay stations around the Polar sea. Many details remain to be evaluated first, however, such as the speed of the dirigibles, their endurance, the size of the crew and the payload, and, above all, the cost of the project based upon them.

## Atmospheric studies in the Space Age

Clearly the earth's atmosphere will be scrutinised in ever-increasing detail as the years pass. It will probably be that the role of the human weather observer will be simultaneously eroded. As in so many other fields of science the technologist holds the key to the future. The interrogation of automatic stations by satellites will probably lead to a greater centralisation of meteorological offices, where computers will continue to take over tasks previously performed manually. Information from the farthest corners of the earth will be automatically received, and fed into computers, whence analyses of various atmospheric patterns will emerge, along with numerical weather predictions. All of these will be plotted out as automatically compiled maps.

International co-operation will be extended under the auspices of the World Meteorological Organisation, and Space vehicles will be contributed by several countries in addition to the U.S.A., for example meteorological rockets by Britain and France, and weather satellites by the Soviet Union. The first known Russian weather satellite, designated COSMOS 122, and similar in appearance and purpose to the NIMBUS type, was put into orbit on June 25th 1966, a few weeks before a W.M.O.—sponsored Training Seminar on the Interpretation and Use of Meteorological Satellite Data was held in Moscow, attended by many scientists from Europe and elsewhere. A.P.T. stations for the American satellites are scattered throughout the world from McMurdo Sound in Antarctica to Frobisher in Northern Canada, and from the Meteorological Office at Bracknell, Berkshire to the Royal Observatory in Hong Kong. The study of weather from Space has grown, in only six years, from a tentative experiment to a world-wide concern.

In the preceding chapters a distinction will have been apparent between pure and applied meteorology, between the research and the forecasting aspects of the atmospheric sciences. Despite increased automation, openings for workers will continue to exist in both, but especially in weather research. The volume of weather data grows larger daily, and will continue to grow. The amount of information yielded by weather satellites in their first six years has been so vast that most of it never will be scrutinised in detail. The range of research topics that spring to mind in this field of satellite meteorology is already very broad, as the few selected suggestions in this book may have indicated. And there is ample scope, too, for more purely geographical research. Many features of man's physical environment can now be studied statistically, and need no longer be described in rather vague qualitative terms.

Even in weather forecasting, much remains to be done manually. It will be some years before computers will be programmed to forecast actual weather itself—the abiding interest of the great majority of consumers. Forecasters are still needed in the provincial offices to apply their more detailed knowledge of local topographical influences upon local weather to suggest how the general forecasts must be modified for broadcasting to different regions. Even in the U.S. Weather Bureau, where the forecasting procedure is the most highly automatic in the world, regular meetings of forecasters are held to assess the validity of computed prognostic charts. The computer programmes do not always give the right answers, representing as they do gross generalisations of the highly complex, very changeable medium of the atmosphere. Trained scientists will continue to be required, not only to ascertain that the computer is producing logical results, to forecast weather, and to make allowances for the local effects of topography, but also, increasingly, to analyse new data types such as infra-red maps and nephanalyses and to devise ways of incorporating their contents into the existing forecasting procedures.

'Problems' have formed a recurrent theme in this final chapter and throughout the book, but they are different from those of six years ago. Definite advances have been made in weather study as a result of the adoption by the meteorologist of that uniquely twentieth-century viewpoint out in Space. The floodgates of knowledge have been further opened by Space technology. The theoretical scientist is being confronted with a swelling flood of material which must be sifted and analysed, compared and collated in an attempt to resolve the atmospheric problems that remain. The end-products should be of practical benefit to the whole of mankind: forecasts will become more accurate, so that the extremes of weather can be met with a greater preparedness, and the normal conditions put to better use. In many parts of the world the weather today is still something to be endured and overcome, and its control by man remains the ultimate goal.

The question that is always put to the meteorologist in times of exceptionally bad weather is not 'why should this be so', but 'what are you doing about it?' This latter question is, unfortunately, premature, for it is not often that a satisfactory answer can be given to the query 'why?' Satellites are important tools in the study of the weather because observation precedes comprehension, and comprehension is a prerequisite of control. We are moving towards this final revolution in weather study, but as yet it is scarcely in sight.

BIBLIOGRAPHY

It is impossible to list a comprehensive bibliography here, since many of the systems mentioned in Chapter 10 have only been described in technical notes and contractors' reports. Two general accounts must suffice. See S. Fritz *et al.*, *Synoptic Use of Meteorological Data and Prospects for the Future*, U.S. Department of Commerce report, Washington, April 1965, prepared for the 17th session of the Executive Committee of the World Meteorological Organisation; and J.S. Sawyer, 'Meteorological analysis—a challenge for the future', *Quarterly Journal of the Royal Meteorological Society*, **90**, 1965, 227.

# Tables

Table 1. Weather Satellite Summary from 1960 to the completion of the first Operational Satellite System in February 1966

| Satellite | Launch date | Orbital period (mins) | Inclination to Equator (°'s) | Apogee (st mi) | Perigee (st mi) | Orientation | Camera types* |
|---|---|---|---|---|---|---|---|
| Tiros I | Apr 1st 1960 | 99·2 | 48·4 | 465·9 | 428·7 | Space | (1) NA |
|  |  |  |  |  |  |  | (1) WA |
| Tiros II | Nov 23rd 1960 | 98·3 | 48·5 | 453·0 | 387·0 | Space | (1) WA |
|  |  |  |  |  |  |  | (1) NA |
| Tiros III | July 12th 1961 | 100·4 | 47·8 | 506·4 | 461·0 | Space | (2) WA |
| Tiros IV | Feb 8th 1962 | 100·4 | 48·3 | 524·8 | 441·2 | Space | (1) MA |
|  |  |  |  |  |  |  | (1) WA |
| Tiros V | June 19th 1962 | 100·5 | 58·1 | 603·9 | 366·4 | Space | (1) WA |
|  |  |  |  |  |  |  | (1) MA |
| Tiros VI | Sept 18th 1962 | 98·7 | 58·3 | 442·1 | 425·3 | Space | (1) WA |
|  |  |  |  |  |  |  | (1) MA |
| Tiros VII | June 19th 1963 | 97·4 | 58·2 | 403·5 | 386·1 | Space | (2) WA |
| Tiros VIII | Dec 12th 1963 | 99·4 | 58·5 | 468·0 | 435·0 | Space | (1) WA |
|  |  |  |  |  |  |  | (1) APT |
| Tiros IX | Jan 22nd 1965 | 119·2 | 96·4 | 1601·1 | 420·3 | Cartwheel | (2) WA |
| Tiros X | July 2nd 1965 | 100·7 | 98·7 | 498·8 | 441·3 | Space | (2) WA |
| Nimbus I | Aug 28th 1964 | 103·5 | 98·7 | 578·0 | 263·0 | Earth | (3) AVC |
|  |  |  |  |  |  |  | (1) APT |
| Essa I | Feb 3rd 1966 | 100·0 | 98·0 | 522·4 | 433·0 | Cartwheel | (2) WA |
| Essa II | Feb 28th 1966 | 113·4 | 101·0 | 882·5 | 840·9 | Cartwheel | (2) APT |

*Camera Types: Narrow angle TV: NA. Medium angle TV: MA. Wide angle TV: WA. Automatic picture taking: APT. Advanced vidicon camera: AVC

*Note:* It is not considered worthwhile to detail the active operational lives of the satellites, since many have continued to supply limited and sporadic data after some of the systems have failed. NIMBUS I only functioned for twenty-six days, whereas TIROS VII is still partially operational after nearly three years. The average life-expectancy is about one year.

## Table 2. TIROS Camera Characteristics

| Parameter | Narrow angle | Medium angle | Wide angle |
|---|---|---|---|
| Lens Angle | 12·5° | 76° | 104° |
| Lens Speed | f/1·8 | f/1·8 | f/1·5 |
| Shutter Speed | 0·0015 seconds | 0·0015 seconds | 0·0015 seconds |
| Object area (viewed vertically from 400 miles) | 70 miles square | 450 miles square | 750 miles square |
| Normal Resolution | 0·2 miles | 1·5 miles | 2·0 miles |

## Table 3. Medium Resolution Infra-red Wavebands Investigated by TIROS Satellites

| Channel | Nominal Spectral Range | Measurement |
|---|---|---|
| 1 | 6·0–6·5μ | Absorption by water vapour |
| 1 (TIROS VII) | 14·5–15·5μ | Absorption by carbon dioxide |
| 2 | 8·0–12·0μ | Major 'atmospheric window' |
| 3 | 0·2–6·0μ | Reflected solar radiation |
| 4 | 7·0–30·0μ | Long-wave radiation back to Space |
| 5 | 0·55–0·75μ | Reflected visible solar radiation |

Table 4. A guide to the Geographical Distribution of Severe Tropical Storms and Hurricanes

| Area | J | F | M | A | M | J | J | A | S | O | N | D | YR. |
|---|---|---|---|---|---|---|---|---|---|---|---|---|---|
| North Atlantic (1887–1955) | – | – | – | – | 0·1 | 0·4 | 0·5 | 1·5 | 2·6 | 1·9 | 0·5 | – | 7·5 |
| N Pacific (off W Coast of Mexico) (1910–40) | – | – | – | – | 0·1 | 0·8 | 0·7 | 1·0 | 1·9 | 1·0 | 0·1 | – | 5·7 |
| N Pacific (W of 170°E) (1901–40) | 0·4 | 0·2 | 0·3 | 0·4 | 0·7 | 1·0 | 3·2 | 4·2 | 4·6 | 3·2 | 1·7 | 1·2 | 21·1 |
| N Indian O (Bay of Bengal) (Period unknown) | 0·1 | – | 0·2 | 0·2 | 0·5 | 0·6 | 0·8 | 0·6 | 0·7 | 0·9 | 1·0 | 0·4 | 6·0 |
| N Indian O (Arabian Sea) (Period unknown) | 0·1 | – | – | 0·1 | 0·2 | 0·3 | 0·1 | – | 0·1 | 0·2 | 0·3 | 0·1 | 1·5 |
| S Indian O (E of Madagascar to 90°E) (Possibly 1839–1922) | 1·3 | 1·7 | 1·2 | 0·6 | 0·2 | – | – | – | – | – | – | 0·1 | 5·1 |
| S Indian O (NW Australia) (Possibly 1839–1922) | 0·3 | 0·2 | 0·2 | 0·1 | – | – | – | – | – | – | – | 0·1 | 0·9 |
| S Pacific Ocean | Data insufficient to compile monthly frequency figures, the maximum concentration apparently being from December–March | | | | | | | | | | | | |
| S Atlantic Ocean | Data Inadequate for tabulation | | | | | | | | | | | | |

The figures represent the average frequencies over the periods stated; frequencies less than 0·1 per month are not shown. (After Dunn & Miller 1960)

## Table 5. A Classification of tropical storms (after Timchalk, Hubert and Fritz).

| Features | Category 0 | Category 1 | Category 2 | Category 3 | Category 4 |
|---|---|---|---|---|---|
| Eye or Pattern Centre. | No Centre in overcast cloud mass. | No eye. Pattern centre poorly defined. Centre can be approximately located by extrapolating inwards from curved band structure. | No eye, but visible pattern centre located at tip of broad curved band which curves at large cross angle towards the centre. | Eye usually visible, but ragged and irregular in shape. No bright continuous circular wall cloud about the eye. | Eye usually visible as dark smooth-edged spot, encircled by a prominent bright ring of wall cloud. |
| Striations. | No striations or radiating cirrus. | No striations in overcast, but some cirrus striations usually found at the edge of the dense cloud region. | Few or no striations in overcast. Some striations, not necessarily radial, found at edge of dense cloud region. | Some curved striations in over cast. Cirrus outflow often visible, curving away from edge of overcast. | Pronounced concentric striations within overcast, and in high cloud outside it. |
| Bands. | No bands to suggest a centre. | Bands not well organised and often obscured by dense cirrus. | Frequently one long band which may spiral through a complete revolution before ending in a broad tip in the centre. The spiral band often merges with a tail, and the overcast area is therefore assymetrical. | Nearly concentric spiral i.e. one which curves inwards at low angles. Narrower than in category 2. | Narrow and nearly concentric spiral bands, with concentricity about the eye wall. Banding outside the main area of overcast is strong and highly organised. |

| | | | | |
|---|---|---|---|---|
| Breaks in Cloudiness. | Random Breaks. | Generally irregular. Non-concentric, breaks. | A linear curved break is characteristic, terminating very close to the broad tipped spiral at the storms centre. | Almost concentric, or highly curved, slightly ragged breaks covered by thin cirrus. | Breaks smoother-edged and more nearly concentric than in Category 3. |
| Additional Miscellaneous Features. | Ragged and ill-defined cloud mass. | Weak cyclonic cloud organisation usually visible outside the dense overcast. The pattern centre area tends to be a dense aggregate of bright cloud. | Broad band organisation usually extends into curving tail. | The overall cloud shape is compact, and tends to be circular despite the probable presence of a tail. | The main circular overcast tends to be smoothly and distinctly edged over one or two quadrants. A clear 'moat' may occur between the overcast, and the strong banding outside it. |

Table 6. Some Terrestrial features that can be distinguished on TIROS photographs without prior knowledge of the area portrayed (After Merifield and Rammelkamp 1966)

| | Feature | Identification Criteria |
|---|---|---|
| 1 | Large bodies of water | These are the darkest land features, with black tone, uniform texture, and sharp outlines. |
| 2 | Large floodplains and deltas | Dark in tone, owing to vegetation. Floodplains follow sinuous paths terminating at large bodies of water. Deltas have a triangular shape with thin bases forming shorelines. |
| 3 | Shoreline beaches and barrier beaches | High albedos along, or parallel to, shorelines. |
| 4 | Desert sand seas and bolsons | High albedos, circular or elongated shapes, associated with playas and dunes. |
| 5 | Playas and barred evaporite basins | Brightest land features, have albedos comparable with clouds. Playas occur within bolsons, and barred basins adjacent to large bodies of water. |
| 6 | Giant seif dunes (greater than 50 km in length) | High albedos, gently curved, long, narrow shapes; associated with sand seas. |
| 7 | Cenozoic orogenic belts in arid or semi-arid regions | Bands of parallel dark and light streaks, usually curved or sinuous. |

Table 7. Remote sensor experiments being studied by NASA, and some of their expected application. (After P.C. Badgley 1965)

| Application Experimental Technique | Agriculture and Forestry | Geology | Hydrology | Oceanography | Geography |
|---|---|---|---|---|---|
| Photography | Soils Vegetation growth Plant disease | Surface structure | Drainage patterns and soil moisture | State of the sea Turbidity, Productivity | Cartography, Land use, Transportation, Terrain and Vegetation etc |
| Infra-red Investigation | Terrain composition Plant condition | Areas of thermal anomaly Mineral distribution | Areas of cooling | Ocean currents and sea ice | Land use |
| Radar Imagery | Soil characteristics | Surface roughness Tectonics | Soil Moisture Run-off slopes | State of the sea Ice characteristics | Snow cover, Cartography Geodesy, Vegetation |
| Microwave Radiometry | Thermal state of terrain | Sub-surface layering | Snow and ice | | Snow and ice |
| Remote Geo-chemical Testing | | Mineral deposits Trace elements | | Surface flora | |

# Index